A Truth in Science Publication

Origins
Examining the Evidence

Geoff Barnard
Andy McIntosh
Steve Taylor

Origins: Examining the Evidence

First printed in November 2011
ISBN: 978-0-9569631-0-9
Published by Truth in Science

Cover design and typesetting by Dave Hewer Design
(davehewer.com).

Contents Overview

For fuller breakdown of the contents, please see next page.

Contents Detail

For briefer breakdown of the contents, please see previous page.

Foreword
Professor Andy McIntosh

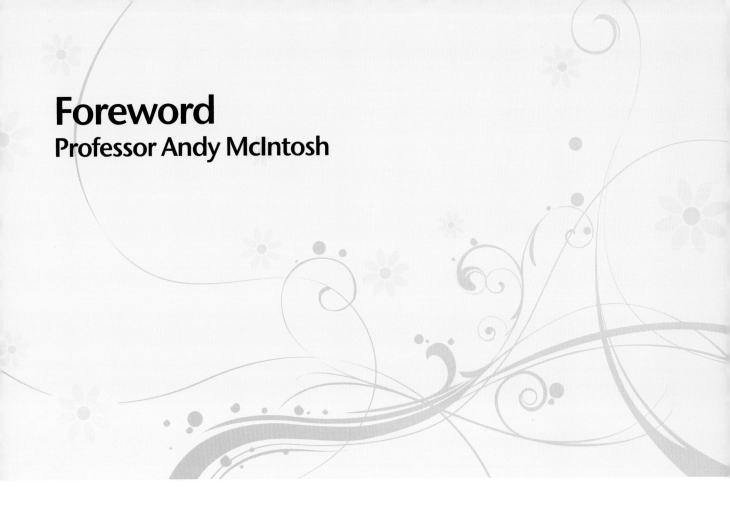

In September 2008, Michael Reiss was removed from his position as director of education at the Royal Society. What was his crime? Had he suggested that creationism should be taught in schools? No, he believes firmly in evolution. Had he advocated alternatives be taught alongside evolution? No, for like many in charge of education today, he would not accept that there is any scientific alternative. What then was his thinking that caused such a cry for his scalp? Simply that creation should be treated as a worldview rather than a misconception, and be discussed openly in the classroom.[1]

The furore that this caused demonstrates the bigoted nature of some who would close down all debate on the basis that they know the scientific truth. How ironic that the motto of the Royal Society[2] is "Nullius in verba"; that is "On the word of no one" or, in more colloquial language, "Take nobody's word for it".

This motto was taken up in 1663, three years after the official inception of the Royal Society[2] with the patronage of Charles II. In the words of the Society's own website, the whole purpose behind the motto was "to withstand the domination of authority" and "to verify all statements by an appeal to facts determined by experiment".

Several scientists who have no time for non-evolutionary thinking were deeply embarrassed by what the Royal Society did that day. Lord Winston, well known for his fertility work, said:

> I fear that in this action the Royal Society may have only diminished itself. This is not a good day for the reputation of science or scientists. This individual was arguing that we should engage with and address public misconceptions about science – something that the Royal Society should applaud.[1]

"I am shocked about what happened with the Royal Society", said Leslie Jones, Professor of Biology at Valdosta State University in Georgia, and even Professor Dawkins had to admit: "To call for his resignation... comes a little too close to a witch-hunt for my squeamish taste".

The *Nature News* article of 17th September[3] which reported these comments expresses the view that Reiss was not out of step with the Royal Society (and thus its motto), but then goes on to quote Sir Harold Kroto, who unwittingly reveals the prejudice at the heart of this matter.

Reiss's remarks, he says, seemed fairly reasonable - if uttered by a freethinker for whom evidence-based philosophy is pre-eminent.

In other words according to Kroto, you have to be a freethinker to be a scientist and *Nullius in verba* only applies to throwing off the shackles of deistic/theistic belief. When the boot is on the other foot *Nullius in verba* does not apply!

The *Nature* editorial of 25th September[4] wisely stated:

> At such a moment, a much more effective approach is for the teacher to follow the route Reiss advocated: deal with the question without ridicule, but make it clear that in science, theories must be testable to be valid.

We heartily agree. There is no fear in scientific debate from our side. It is not the place of the scientific classroom to bring in religious instruction but neither is it the place to propagate the blind belief in atheistic philosophy. It would seem very evident that some influential evolutionists seem to have a real phobia about genuine scientific debate.

The editorial in *Nature*[4] refers to Eugenie Scott, no friend of Intelligent Design or Creation thinking:

> Eugenie Scott, executive director of the National Center for Science Education in Oakland, California, and a long-time advocate for the teaching of evolution, points out that in the real world, any such shut-up-and-take-it-elsewhere response from the teacher will inevitably be perceived by the student (and his or her classmates) as a humiliating personal put-down. It will obstruct rather than encourage enquiry

and understanding. It will also invite complaints from outraged parents... What is more; it will squander what experienced educators like to call 'a teachable moment'. All too often, that moment is the one opportunity that a school has to engage resistant students and introduce them to what science has to say.

The editorial went on to quote a biology teacher in Florida who stated:

> Biology graduates who have not encountered up-to-date evidence of evolution in action - in fossils, in microbes, in genomes - have been ill-served by their training. Higher education in general and biology departments in particular, are at the front line of the battle between creation and evolution too.

It is all too often the case that a proper detailed knowledge of the actual fossil evidence is lacking. We come to different conclusions than those advocated by the biology teacher and the *Nature* editorial, but we join with their wise counsel: that the evidence needs to be put before teachers and students.

We think, in fact, that many will actually see for themselves that the evolutionary hypothesis is not yet substantiated. We have already advocated in 2006 that the DVD "Where does the evidence lead?" be watched by all UK schools, and we encourage all science classes to consider carefully the evidence itself without prejudice to either view, rather than the philosophical assumptions of evolutionary thinkers imposed upon the evidence.

Natural selection is not the same as evolution. Natural selection is a verifiable fact of the biological world, but there is no power in natural selection ever shown experimentally in the laboratory to change and add machinery which was not there already, either in coded form or latently in the genetic information stored in the genomic template – that is what evolutionary philosophy has advocated but which is not consistent with the evidence. This is why the debate will not go away. Clearly we all know it has philosophical overtones, but the scientific debate has to be allowed to proceed, to enable pupils and students to understand the scientific issues.

A most perceptive comment[3] came on line after the *Nature News* editorial from Michael Buratovich on the 23rd September 2008:

> Removing him because he dared bring up the 'C' word simply demonstrates that some of the British science intelligentsia fail to understand that we are not going to advance understanding of evolution by ignoring creationism. Patient engagement in the classroom is certainly one of the ways to address this issue. What is so wrong with that?

Indeed, we might well ask. What is it that the Royal Society and others are so afraid of in the classroom, if indeed the evidence is so powerful for evolution? What can possibly be lost by looking at the evidence without *a priori* assumptions of creation, design or atheism? Are our schools to become places of atheistic "freethinking" indoctrination? Truth in Science are seeking to redress the balance. For too long, educational materials have been heavily biased with a philosophy which predisposes children to come to evolutionary conclusions based frankly on teacher and peer pressure.

It has never been the view of Truth in Science that creationism should be taught in schools - rather that a critical appraisal of the evolutionary interpretation of the evidence be put forward so that the student can "follow where the evidence leads", once they have been taught the basic laws of physics and chemistry and the fundamental, experimentally-verifiable biochemical laws. Then, simply faced with experimental evidence, the student can make a considered judgment as to which thesis best fits the evidence.

The more vigorously those of an evolutionary persuasion insist that the only correct paradigm with which to approach science is atheistic, the further away we have drifted from the Royal Society motto. Some of the leading scientists of the Royal Society down the centuries have been theists. Isaac Newton, Robert Boyle, Lord Kelvin – are all these to be downgraded because they had this troubling belief in the divine? Why should today's thinkers be any different? Has the evidence so indisputably removed the need for the divine, or is it just prejudice?

We would ask our readers to think carefully about the scientific evidence. We are ardent in our desire that the evidence should speak for itself. Atheistic humanism is as much of a danger to true scientific activity as the overbearing scholasticism of the 17th century, when the Royal Society was formed. If we stifle genuine scientific debate now we will lose the Faradays, Maxwells and Keplers of tomorrow.

Professor Andy McIntosh
Leeds
November 2011

Foreword Endnotes

1   http://www.telegraph.co.uk/news/newstopics/religion/2971456/Royal-Society-scientist-loses-post-in-row-over-creationism-in-schools.html

2   http://royalsociety.org/page.asp?id=6186

3   Editorial (17th September 2008) *Creationism stir fries Reiss* Nature News http://www.nature.com/news/2008/080917/full/news.2008.1116.html

4   Editorial (25th September 2008) *Creation and classrooms* Nature 455:431-2

CHAPTER 1
Everything from Nothing?

1.1 What is Evolution?

Evolution is remarkably difficult to define precisely, as it means so many different things to different people. Douglas Futuyama, a respected evolutionary biologist, has defined biological evolution as follows:

> Biological (or organic) evolution is change in the properties of populations of organisms or groups of such populations, over the course of generations. The development, or ontogeny, of an individual organism is not considered evolution: individual organisms do not evolve. The changes in populations that are considered evolutionary are those that are 'heritable' via the genetic material from one generation to the next.

Biological evolution may be slight or substantial; it embraces everything from slight changes in the proportions of different forms of a gene within a population, such as the alleles that determine the different human blood types, to the alterations that led from the earliest organisms to dinosaurs, bees, snapdragons, and humans.[1]

According to this definition, any genetic changes that can be inherited by offspring and that can spread throughout the population of that organism over time can be considered as evolution. In principle, these changes can be great or subtle, on a large scale or on a small scale.

1.2 Evolution on a Large Scale (sometimes referred to as Macroevolution)

Mark Ridley has defined macroevolution as follows:

> Macroevolution means evolution on the grand scale, and it is mainly studied in the fossil

record. It is contrasted with microevolution, the study of evolution over short time periods, such as that of a human lifetime or less. Microevolution therefore refers to changes in gene frequency within a population ... Macroevolutionary events are more likely to take millions, probably tens of millions of years. Macroevolution refers to things like the trends in horse evolution described by Simpson, and occurring over tens of millions of years, or the origin of major groups, or mass extinctions, or the Cambrian explosion described by Conway Morris. Speciation is the traditional dividing line between micro- and macroevolution.[2]

In these two definitions, we see something of the difficulty in trying to define the term "evolution". Ridley distinguishes between macroevolution and microevolution in terms of speciation. Any genetic change that ultimately leads to the origin of new species is macroevolution.

1.3 Variation within Species (sometimes referred to as Microevolution)

Both definitions indicate that any change in gene frequencies in a population is evolutionary. These changes may or may not lead to the development of new species. The classic case is the peppered moth, where dark and light varieties may be present in a single population. When environmental changes take place which give one form a higher survival potential or simply more offspring than another, inevitably there will be an alteration in the gene frequencies of the population leading to one form predominating over the other.

Origin of new structures and functions (evolution)

In this book we reserve the term "evolution" for changes which bring into being new structures and functions. The small changes referred to above are simply an example of variation, and are not examples of evolution according to our definition.

Variation can be seen everywhere. Within every species there is considerable variety. We see this clearly in our own species. That variety is driven by differences in the expression of genes. When the environment favours one form over another, there will tend to be a change in the abundance of each variety. Those that are better adapted to the environment will produce more offspring and thus be "more fit" than those that are less well adapted.

1.4 What then is a Species?

A species is generally defined as a group of organisms that have sufficiently similar characteristics and, most particularly, can interbreed with one another to produce viable and fertile offspring. Let us further consider the case of the peppered moth (*Biston betularia*). Although, this insect is often used as an example of evolution in action, nobody has yet suggested that the light and dark varieties are separate species. Apart from coloration, the two varieties are essentially identical and may interbreed. Whether they actually interbreed is uncertain since the dark

or light form may prefer a mate with similar coloration.

However, if the light or the dark forms of the moth were to become totally geographically isolated from each other; they might also become reproductively isolated from each other (unable to produce viable fertile offspring by interbreeding) over a sufficient period of time. If so, the two varieties would then be regarded as separate species. Reproductive isolation has a genetic aspect and, in the case of higher animals, may involve divergent behaviour such as sexual displays (e.g. coloration, song and dance motifs etc.) and also chemical signalling (e.g. pheromones). In this case, groups of organisms may look identical and be physiologically capable of interbreeding to produce viable fertile offspring, but fail to mate for behavioural reasons. Thus different species cannot always be recognised by a casual observer.

In general, organisms with fundamentally different genomes cannot interbreed to produce viable and fertile offspring. This is one of the biggest problems for the evolutionary scientist to consider. We could say it is not just the survival of the fittest, but the survival of the fertile.

1.5 What is Natural Selection?

The Peppered Moth is often used as an example of evolution in action (Photo: Andy Phillips/Flickr)

Natural selection is a consequence of certain varieties being more able than others to cope with environmental pressure. Again, let us consider the example of the peppered moth. Following the Industrial Revolution, it has been suggested that the dark form of the moth was less visible on the darkened bark of trees. On the other hand, the lighter form of the moth was more vulnerable to bird predation. Consequently, over a fairly short period of time, there was a change in the frequency of the dark versus the light variety, and of the gene form (allele) that produces dark moths.

In the case of the peppered moth, we do not know how the two forms originated. Variation within each species is a fact of life. However, random genetic mutations do occur, and if these lead to alterations in gene expression, there will be new variation and perhaps new varieties. If these new varieties are more suited to any given environment, natural selection will tend to favour them and may cause them to predominate. It must be emphasised that evolution is not the theory that variation occurs; rather it is the theory that there is no taxonomic limit to the changes that variation can bring about. Evidence for the former does not confirm the latter.

The dispute over evolution is whether these genetic fluctuations that are characteristic of individual species can, over vast periods of time, drive the formation of radically different species by natural selection. The dilemma is highlighted by Larry Moran of the University of Toronto:

Nobody denies that macroevolutionary processes involve the fundamental mechanisms of natural selection and random genetic drift, but these microevolutionary processes are not sufficient, by themselves, to explain the history of life. That's why, in the domain of macroevolution, we encounter theories about species sorting and tracking, species selection, and punctuated equilibria.[3]

1.6 What is Common Descent?

Charles Darwin (Photo: ©)

The evidence provided for microevolution - which is strong - is generally extrapolated to substantiate the claim that over vast eons of time minor random changes by mutation and other genetic alterations can explain the emergence of all life forms from one or a few primordial ancestors. This is eloquently described by Darwin himself in the conclusion of *On the Origin of Species*:

There is a grandeur in this view of life, with its several powers, having been originally breathed into a few forms or into one; and that whilst this planet has gone cycling on according to the fixed law of gravity, from so simple a beginning endless forms most beautiful and most wonderful have been, and are being, evolved.[4]

Evolutionary scientists hold differing views as to the possibility of more than one common ancestor. As we have seen, Darwin himself was uncertain as to whether life was "originally breathed into a few forms or into one". Others would maintain that the origin of life is so improbable that it is only possible to conceive of one event, a singularity. However, some evolutionary scientists believe the opposite, that given the right conditions, life is inevitable. For example, this is one reason why there are expeditions to Mars. If we can discover water plus other essential elements, there is the real expectation that evidence of at least microbial life will be found.

Accordingly, some scientists believe that life may have had more than one origin. The arguments against this proposal include the existence of a common and universal genetic code. This is not quite the case, as research indicates some divergence in the genetic code in certain micro-organisms, but the claim is substantially true.

The fundamental issue is not whether there have been one or several origins of life, but whether the principle of microevolution based on genetic (allelic) variation within a population leading to a changing gene pool through natural selection and genetic drift can be extrapolated to explain the major changes to structures and functions necessary for the emergence of completely new species and new kinds of living creatures.

For example, can a fish species develop a terrestrial physiology by random mutation and differential survival alone? As Moran states: "Microevolutionary processes are not sufficient, by themselves, to explain the history of life". This is not a trivial problem and explains why evolutionary biologists hold radically different views from one another. On the one hand, we have Richard Dawkins who has stated:

> We have seen that living things are too improbable and too beautifully 'designed' to have come into existence by chance. How, then, did they come into existence? The answer, Darwin's answer, is by gradual, step-by-step transformations from simple beginnings, from primordial entities sufficiently simple to have come into existence by chance. Each successive change in the gradual evolutionary process was simple enough, relative to its predecessor, to have arisen by chance. But the whole sequence of cumulative steps constitutes anything but a chance process, when you consider the complexity of the final end-product relative to the original starting point. The cumulative process is directed by nonrandom survival.[5]

On the other hand, we have Stephen Gould, who proposed (with Niles Eldridge) the theory of punctuated equilibrium. Gould's disquiet with classical Darwinism is clearly seen in his 1977 essay, *Return of the Hopeful Monster*, in which he supports the earlier work of geneticist Richard Goldschmidt. In this essay, Gould writes:

> Indeed, if we do not invoke discontinuous change by small alteration in rates of development, I do not see how most major evolutionary transitions can be accomplished at all. Few systems are more resistant to basic change than the strongly differentiated, highly specified, complex adults of "higher" animal groups. How could we ever convert an adult rhinoceros or a mosquito into something fundamentally different? Yet transitions between major groups have occurred in the history of life.[6]

An ammonite of the genus Hoploscaphites
(Photo: DanielCD/Wikimedia)

As we will see, the problem for evolutionary theory on the grand scale (i.e. macroevolution) is lack of observable evidence in the real world. This is particularly true when we consider the evolution of micro-organisms. One hundred and fifty years of intense bacteriological research has not documented the emergence of new species. The only evidence for macroevolution that can be considered is that from the fossil record. Nevertheless, the process of fossilisation is associated with catastrophic events. In other words, the fossil record is a series of catastrophic snapshots that can equally be interpreted as documenting species change or unchanging species that are sporadically and selectively preserved. The debate continues and is summarised succinctly by Ernst Mayer:

> Among all the claims made during the evolutionary synthesis, perhaps the one that found least acceptance, was the assertion that all phenomena of macroevolution can be 'reduced to', that is, explained by, microevolutionary genetic processes. Not surprisingly, this claim was usually supported by geneticists but was widely rejected by the very biologists who dealt with macroevolution, the morphologists and paleontologists. Many of them insisted that there

is more or less complete discontinuity between the processes at the two levels—that what happens at the species level is entirely different from what happens at the level of the higher categories. Now, 50 years later, the controversy remains undecided.[7]

1.7 What do the Textbooks say?

School and university textbooks generally reflect these uncertainties. The evidence that is presented to support the Darwinian hypothesis can be divided into large-scale evolution and small-scale variation. Apart from the fossil record, large-scale changes are illustrated by reference to origin-of-life studies, molecular and anatomical homology and references to embryology, most of which is speculation.

On the other hand, much is made in the textbooks of adaptation and genetic drift in populations. The peppered moth and Darwin's finches feature prominently. In this book, we will look at this evidence from a critical perspective.

The objective of this publication is to advocate a more critical approach to Darwinism by considering honestly not only the evidence for but also evidence against the theory. Primarily, we believe that a more critical approach will lead to an openness of mind which will produce better scientists and will allow room for scientists to be intellectually fulfilled agnostics with respect to evolutionary theory, while being much more modest in our assessment of what we do and do not know.

1.8 Worldview Considerations

How do scientists establish their conclusions? How do we know anything is actually true? How can we be sure that what we are told is a trustworthy foundation upon which to build? These are important questions with which we must wrestle in an age of increasing scepticism. What we discover when we begin to probe a little beneath the surface is that each one of us consciously or unwittingly approaches everyday experience with certain presuppositions.

Collectively, these foundational beliefs constitute a worldview, which governs our whole outlook on life. In particular, a worldview determines (a) our notion of what the world is really like; (b) how we know anything (epistemology); and (c) a basis for determining right from wrong (ethics).

Philosophers have historically differed in their own particular starting places, their first premises. It is important to note that the modern approach to "scientific reasoning" has increasingly placed confidence on man's autonomous exercise of "reason" and an

Philosopher David Hume (Photo: ©)

inductive enterprise known as "the scientific method".

The authors of this publication positively encourage the proper use of reason in science.

But we also dare to raise important questions regarding its underlying philosophical foundations (i.e. presuppositions). For instance, we want to interrogate the modern naturalistic approach of science to know why we should adopt a principle of uniformity. Why suppose that processes in the future will operate as in the past? One can say that B follows A, but it is not possible to be certain that it always has or always will.

Or why should arguments which move from particular observations to universal generalisations be valid at all? These are crucial and valid concerns. The philosopher David Hume stated that we cannot see causation. Should we say that A necessarily causes B simply because B happens to follow A on many occasions? Or should we say that A causes B because B does not happen if we prevent A from happening?

We are told by those who hold a naturalistic worldview that ultimate reality comprises only matter and energy emanating from a primordial "big bang". But if the ultimate reality is so bare and mindless, what kind of things are logic and reason? Charles Darwin himself wrote:

> With me, the horrid doubt always arises whether the convictions of man's mind, which has been developed from the mind of the lower animals, are of any value or at all trustworthy. Would any one trust in the convictions of a monkey's mind, if there are any convictions in such a mind...?[8]

However, it is self-evident that everyone is "hard-wired" to think and evaluate. Every human being has a worldview which profoundly influences how he or she deals with life's events, scientifically or otherwise. We need to re-examine the evidence for evolution without recourse to the *a priori* presumption that evolution is a "fact". We need to distinguish evidence that can be clearly observed from that which is simply assumed to exist, and conclusions that are inferred without evidence.

1.9 Further Questions

One of the challenges associated with this book is that arguments "for and against" the Darwinian hypothesis generate such heated and often polarised debate. Accordingly, at the end of each section there will be a list of a few extra questions to ponder. These are meant as a starting point to encourage the reader to think around the issues raised in the section. For example:

1   What kinds of processes are appropriate to extrapolate over vast periods of time in order to make conclusions about the distant past or the distant future?

2   Can extrapolations over long time periods be tested, verified or disproved? If not, in what ways can they be regarded as scientific?

3   On what basis should we believe extrapolations about macro-evolutionary change on the basis of micro-evolutionary observations to be either valid or invalid?

Chapter 1 Endnotes

1   Futuyma DJ (1998) *Evolutionary Biology* 3rd edition Sinauer Associates Inc
2   Ridley M (1997) *Evolution*, Oxford University Press, Oxford UK
3   http://bioinfo.med.utoronto.ca/Evolution_by_Accident/Macroevolution.html
4   Darwin C (1859) *On the Origin of Species by Means of Natural Selection, or the Preservation of Favoured Races in the Struggle for Life*
5   Dawkins R (1986) *The Blind Watchmaker* Penguin Books, UK, page 43
6   Gould, SJ (1977) *The Return of the Hopeful Monster* Natural History 86:22
7   Mayr E (2001) *Towards a New Philosophy of Biology*, Harvard University Press, Cambridge MA USA
8   Darwin C in Francis Darwin (ed.) *The Life and Letters of Charles Darwin* (1887 ed.) pages 315-6

CHAPTER 2
Life from Chemistry?

2.1 The Miller-Urey Experiment

Charles Darwin recognised that a basic problem for his theory of evolution was to explain the production of life itself. In a letter to Joseph Hooker in 1871, he wrote:

> ... if (and oh! what a big if!) we could conceive [of] some warm little pond, with all sorts of ammonia and phosphoric salts, light, heat, electricity etc. present, that a protein compound was chemically formed ready to undergo still more complex changes, at the present day such matter would be instantly absorbed, which would not have been the case before living creatures were found.[1]

If the whole history of the universe can be explained from a simple beginning by laws of physics, then living organisms have to arise from non-living chemicals. And natural selection only acts on things that replicate themselves and pass on traits to their offspring. So a complete evolutionist view of the universe requires a theory for how living things could arise from non-living chemicals.

This area is known as chemical evolution, or the problem of the origin of life.

1953 was a landmark year for scientists researching an evolutionary explanation for the appearance of life. Stanley Miller reported an experiment in which he attempted to replicate the assumed conditions of the primeval Earth and had produced the chemicals that were essential for life to begin.[2] Extravagant claims were made by some, even that he had synthesised life itself! Over 50 years have now passed, and we can make a sober and scientific assessment of that experiment and others like it. Let us consider first what Miller did and saw.

He assembled a closed system (see Figure 2.1) into which he pumped a mixture of gases (methane [CH_4], ammonia [NH_3] and hydrogen [H_2]). There was a flask of boiling water in order to add water vapour to the mixture and the gases were circulated around the apparatus. The gaseous mixture was subjected to a high voltage electrical discharge and then passed through a condenser to cool it down before going through a "trap" cooled in ice to collect any liquid products. Unchanged material was cycled through the apparatus repeatedly to maximise the yield. The objective was to simulate conditions in which the first living material could have originated from non-living chemicals.

This was a good chemical experiment but was it relevant to the objective? Let's look closely at the detail.

2.2 Inappropriate Conditions

First, consider the gaseous mixture. This was supposed to replicate the primeval atmosphere on the Earth. You will notice that there is an absence of oxygen and nitrogen, which are the main elemental constituents of our present environment. The problem recognised by Miller and his colleagues was that oxygen would destroy any organic material in the experiment and certainly in the period of time they allocated to the early period on the planet. For example, when we die, we decay. A part of that process (in addition to bacterial action) is the oxidation of the organic materials in the body, generating carbon dioxide and water.

Consequently, evolutionary scientists have proposed that the early Earth had no elemental oxygen. It would, in fact, be a "reducing atmosphere", the opposite of the modern oxidising one. (They go on to hypothesise that this would gradually change as primitive life produced oxygen through processes such as photosynthesis). However, the evidence for this reducing atmosphere is very tenuous. Increasingly, we are finding from geological and palaeontological research that an oxygen-based atmosphere must have existed from the earliest times. According to David Bevacqua of Pennsylvania State University:

> Our results suggest that most of the fine-grained hematite crystals in the Towers Formation formed by rapid mixing of Fe^{2+}-rich hydrothermal solutions with O_2-rich bottom waters. Furthermore, the presence of an oxygenated deep sea implies a fully oxygenated atmosphere at 3.46 Ga [billion years].[3]

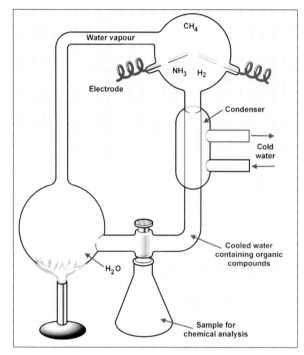

Figure 2.1 Stanley Miller's Apparatus

Various other alternative atmospheres have been proposed, but these either do not generate the materials required or are faced with similar problems to those mentioned for Miller's work. Furthermore, without oxygen in the primeval atmosphere, there would be no development of the protective ozone layer around the earth. Without this protection, intense cosmic and ultra-violet radiation might easily destroy any simple living organisms.

2.3 Irrelevant Method

As we have seen, the atmosphere used was inappropriate. In fact, the experimental method was also irrelevant for explaining the origin of life. First, we have to ask about the circulatory system Miller used for building up significant quantities of chemicals. How could we get the cooling systems that are needed to isolate the products and protect them from further reaction? Second, what was the source of energy? Miller used electrical discharges and compared them to lightning. Others have argued that the sun provides large amounts of continuous energy (which is used today in photosynthesis, for example). This, they claim, could synthesise the required chemicals over extended periods of time. But this theory overlooks the third and most important problem. Basically, this argument is saying:

Raw Materials + Energy = Life Molecules

An important factor is omitted. In any process that leads to complexity there must be an information source. For example, in photosynthesis a complex system involving chlorophyll captures energy from the sun and uses it to build molecules from raw materials. Can you imagine shaking a flask containing the basic materials for the production of a living cell (amino acids, sugars, nucleotides, fatty acids, etc.) and continuing to do so until a cell appeared? That is essentially what we are requiring in an undirected synthesis of this type. "Shake it more vigorously and for longer" is not a recipe for success!

2.4 Low Yield

So what about the results of Miller's experiment? He obtained a "soup" that contained amino acids and a number of other organic compounds produced in small quantities. Amino acids have the general structure shown in Figure 2.2.

H is a hydrogen atom, COOH is an acidic group, NH_2 is an amino group and R represents a variety of organic groups that can be inserted.

Such amino acids (20 different ones occur in most living organisms – see Figure 2.3) can be joined through their acidic and amino groups to give proteins. These in turn are fundamental to the structure of living organisms (muscles, skin, hair, etc.) and to their biochemical activities (through enzymes). Chemically, this group of molecules in living organisms is the simplest to produce. Attempts to produce other materials of this sort have been less successful – but we can imagine the excitement with which Miller's work was received.

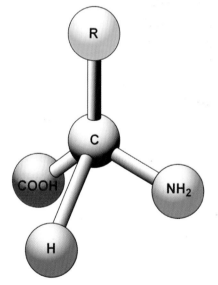

Figure 2.2 General structure of an amino acid

All of the molecules in Figure 2.3 share the basic structure of Figure 2.2 but they have differing properties that allow the construction of an endless variety of proteins.

One of the causes of the low yield was the amino acids reacting with reducing sugars

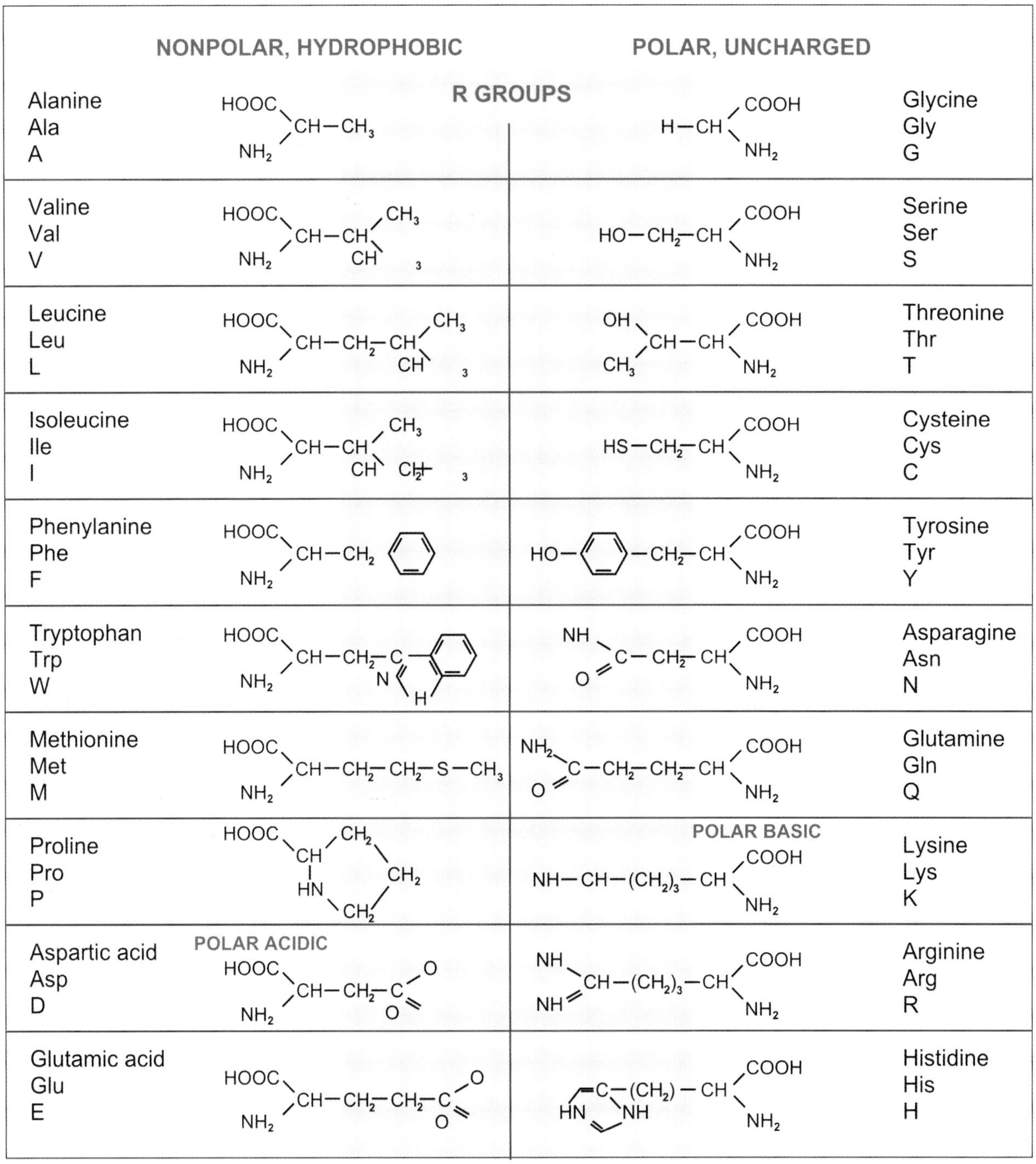

NONPOLAR, HYDROPHOBIC		POLAR, UNCHARGED	
	R GROUPS		
Alanine Ala A	$HOOC$ $\diagdown$ $CH-CH_3$ NH_2	$H-CH$ $\diagup COOH$ $\diagdown NH_2$	Glycine Gly G
Valine Val V	$HOOC$ $\diagdown CH-CH$ NH_2 CH_3 CH_3	$HO-CH_2-CH$ $\diagup COOH$ $\diagdown NH_2$	Serine Ser S
Leucine Leu L	$HOOC$ $\diagdown CH-CH_2-CH$ NH_2 CH_3 CH_3	OH $CH-CH$ $\diagup COOH$ CH_3 $\diagdown NH_2$	Threonine Thr T
Isoleucine Ile I	$HOOC$ $\diagdown CH-CH$ NH_2 CH_3 CH CH_2	$HS-CH_2-CH$ $\diagup COOH$ $\diagdown NH_2$	Cysteine Cys C
Phenylanine Phe F	$HOOC$ $\diagdown CH-CH_2$ NH_2 ⬡	$HO-$⬡$-CH_2-CH$ $\diagup COOH$ $\diagdown NH_2$	Tyrosine Tyr Y
Tryptophan Trp W	$HOOC$ $\diagdown CH-CH_2-C$ NH_2 N H	NH $C-CH_2-CH$ O $\diagup COOH$ $\diagdown NH_2$	Asparagine Asn N
Methionine Met M	$HOOC$ $\diagdown CH-CH_2-CH_2-S-CH_3$ NH_2	NH_2 $C-CH_2-CH_2-CH$ O $\diagup COOH$ $\diagdown NH_2$	Glutamine Gln Q
Proline Pro P	$HOOC$ CH CH_2 HN CH_2 CH_2	POLAR BASIC $NH-CH-(CH_2)_3-CH$ $\diagup COOH$ $\diagdown NH_2$	Lysine Lys K
Aspartic acid Asp D	POLAR ACIDIC $HOOC$ $\diagdown CH-CH_2-C$ NH_2 O O	NH $CH-(CH_2)_3-CH$ NH $\diagup COOH$ $\diagdown NH_2$	Arginine Arg R
Glutamic acid Glu E	$HOOC$ $\diagdown CH-CH_2-CH_2-C$ NH_2 O O	$C-(CH_2)-CH$ HN NH $\diagup COOH$ $\diagdown NH_2$	Histidine His H

Figure 2.3 The 20 Amino Acids found in Living Organisms

in the Maillard reaction, forming a brown tar around Miller's apparatus (see Figure 2.4). Ultimately, Miller was producing large quantities of a brown-coloured compound called melanoidin.

2.5 Wrong Forms of Amino Acids

But there is a more fundamental problem with this scenario, which can easily be overlooked. Amino acids, like all chemicals, are three-dimensional structures. The arrangement of the central carbon atom is tetrahedral[4] (see Figure 2.2). However, in Figure 2.5 you can see two versions of this. Unless you are used to studying these sorts of arrangements, you

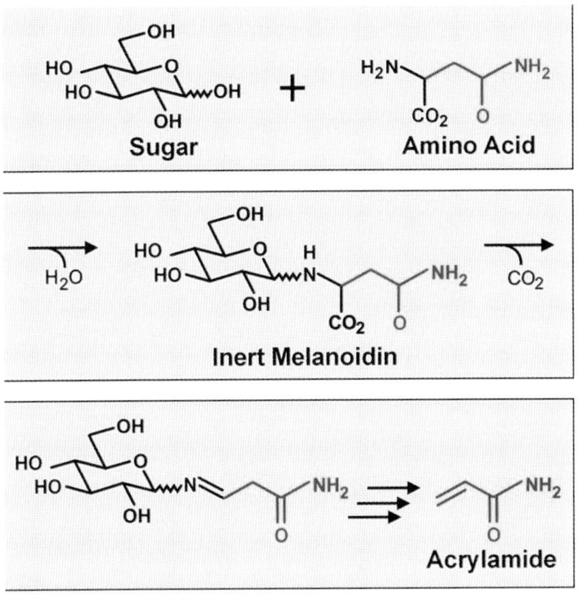

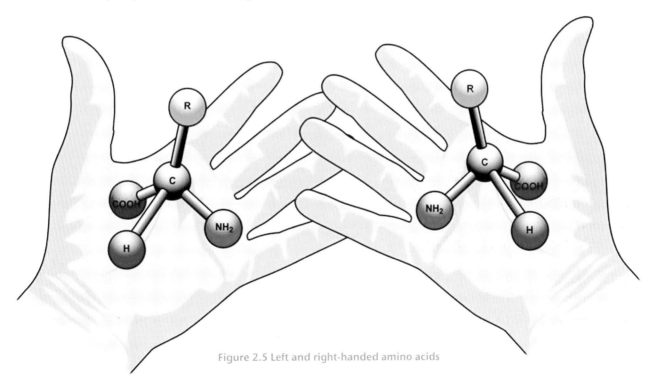

Figure 2.4 The Maillard Reaction

Sugar

Amino Acid

Inert Melanoidin

Acrylamide

the simplest amino acid glycine). Miller's experiment gave a mixture of both forms but nature requires the *levo* form only. Again, does it matter? Functional proteins cannot contain more than traces of right-handed (*dextro*) amino acids. Right-handed forms (*dextro*) can have very different, even fatal, effects in some circumstances.

It is not a simple process to separate them and no-one has discovered a physical system that can do so. In fact, L-amino acids have a tendency to convert chemically to the D-form by a process called *racemization*. This racemization occurs in nature and can cause severe problems. For example, teeth and eye proteins racemize with age and so affect their health; Alzheimer's disease also may be caused by racemization of a specific protein. In addition, the drug thalidomide was produced to aid pregnant mothers in order to combat "morning sickness". It was very effective but sadly led to serious deformities in many babies. One of the reasons was that the commercial drug was sold as a mixture of both left and right-handed forms.

So, we see in this first-stage experiment that we have irrelevant conditions, irrelevant methods, low yields of chemicals in the wrong

might think they are the same; it would seem that you could just rotate one to get the other. But if you look carefully you will see that this is not, in fact, the case. We compare them to our hands by using the terms right-handed and left-handed. And a left-handed glove will not fit on a right hand, for example.

Does this matter? The answer is a very loud "Yes"! In living organisms, we only have left-handed (*levo*) amino acids (apart from

Figure 2.5 Left and right-handed amino acids

proportions and a serious structural problem. If other compounds necessary to life were present (indeed any other compounds at all), we would also have the problem of competitive reactions effectively lowering the yields even further.

2.6 The Problem of Building a Protein

We can see that the process of chemical evolution has failed at the first hurdle. But, in order to get a complete picture, let us assume the problem can be solved (and no-one has done this yet!). We now need the amino acids to join together (*polymerise*) to form proteins.

Here again we have a string of problems. Let us start with the basic chemical one. To link the small molecules together, we need to remove water molecules between adjacent amino acid molecules. This is an equilibrium reaction, which does not occur spontaneously, and the yield of protein depends on removing the water. But, the scenario pictured by evolutionary scientists is one that occurs in a pool of water! Not a promising start! Miller and his colleagues summed up the position themselves:

> Another way of examining this problem is by asking whether there are places on the earth today where we could drop, say, 10 grams of a mixture of amino acids and obtain a significant yield of polypeptides [small proteins]… We cannot think of a single such place.[5]

To form these proteins quickly in the cell, we need accelerators - called enzymes - which enable reactions to occur rapidly (before the cell dies through lack of a protein!). These enzymes enable reactions to occur in milliseconds. Without them, the reactions could take millions, even trillions, of years. The problem is that enzymes are proteins, and they also require enzymes for their own biosynthesis.

But the problems are only just beginning. Another big hurdle lies in the structure of the protein molecule. We have seen that it has to be formed by the joining together of these 20 amino acids. For example, the sequence might begin something like this:

Lys – Ala – His – Gly – Lys –Lys – Val – Leu – Gly – Ala –

where the three letters are shorthand for specific amino acids. In this example, Lys is the amino acid lysine, Ala is alanine, His is histidine, Gly is glycine, Val is valine and Leu is leucine. This chain then twists into a helix. The sequence is called the *primary structure* (see Figure 2.6) and the helix is the *secondary structure*. Other than the fact that the helical structure can twist in one of two directions ("clockwise" or "anticlockwise") and it only takes one of these forms in nature, there is no real problem in this second step.

The helix then folds over on itself to give a more complex structure (*tertiary structure*). This can be imagined most easily by thinking of a floppy spring. If it is released, it will fold over on itself. With the protein chain, there are estimated to be some 100 million different ways it can fold. BUT, only one of these is biologically active.

The correct tertiary structure for each protein is, in turn, dependent on the primary structure: if the amino acid sequence is changed, the structure will fold differently and lose some or all of its activity. An example of this is haemoglobin. This is a large molecule with four protein subunits of two types (alpha and beta) yielding a complex quaternary structure (see Figure 2.6). This protein occurs in our red blood cells and transports oxygen around the body. Just one change in the primary sequence of haemoglobin (a mutation) can convert the red blood cell from its normal shape to a very fragile malformed cell. This happens because one of the subunits of the protein folds into the wrong tertiary structure, and this gives

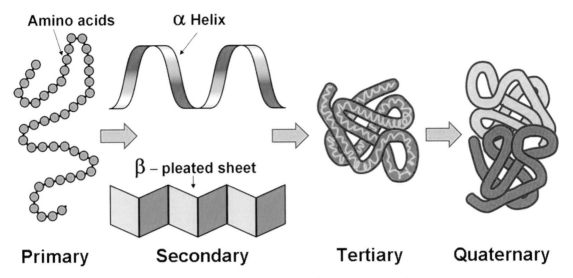

Figure 2.6 Primary, secondary, tertiary and quaternary protein structure

the overall quaternary structure the wrong shape, leading to elongated red blood cells. The resulting change is characteristic of *sickle cell anaemia.*

A person suffering from this disease will die young unless they get regular blood transfusions, but it turns out that a person with one gene for normal haemoglobin and one mutant gene is fairly healthy and is actually more resistant to malaria. The malarial parasite can only live in normal red blood cells, so people who are heterozygous for this mutation actually have a selective advantage in areas where malaria is common.

2.7 Other Chemicals needed for Life

As we examine the other types of chemical in the cell (and they all play important roles), we find the problems tend to become greater than those we have outlined for proteins. For example, complex carbohydrates are formed from sugar molecules and, as with the amino acid to protein conversion, the formation of large carbohydrates from sugars is not spontaneous. Furthermore, sugar molecules are only right-handed (*dextro* form) in nature.

Most scientists acknowledge that these are big problems and that an evolutionary approach has not offered a reasonable scientific explanation for the chemical evolution of the molecules needed for a living cell. We have examined the work of Miller. Of course, other scientists have been involved and have suggested alternative approaches, but these have not overcome the difficulties.

Some scientists have suggested that naturally occurring clays might provide a basis for the original synthesis of biologically relevant molecules. In particular, there has been some speculation that crystal structures in the clays might be considered as "crystal genes" to direct these organic processes. This is an ingenious theory, but it has not been demonstrated scientifically as a means to produce the molecules required for a living cell.

Various other combinations of chemicals have been used as alternatives to Miller's original mixture, but they all have the same problems: a lack of correspondence to the expected composition of the primeval earth, low yields of the products of interest, the destruction of the key compounds by the prevailing conditions or by other chemical by-products, and no explanation for the origins of primordial biological information.

One textbook summarises the situation well:

Despite the simplified account given above, the problem of the origin(s) of life remains. All that has been outlined is speculation and, despite tremendous advances in biochemistry, answers to the problem remain hypothetical… Details of the transition from complex non-living materials to simple living organisms remain a mystery.[6]

In the following case study, we will consider the hypothesis that RNA could have been an important intermediate in the primordial generation of life from chemistry.

2.8 Further Questions

1   Why did Miller exclude oxygen from his experiment?

2   Why is it vital that only left-handed amino acids and right-handed sugars are used in the building of complex biological molecules?

3   Why is it a problem that amino acids can form inert compounds by reacting spontaneously with sugars?

Chapter 2 Endnotes

1   Darwin C in Francis Darwin (ed.) *The Life and Letters of Charles Darwin* (1887 ed.) page 202

2   Miller SL (1953) *Production of Amino Acids under Possible Primitive Earth Conditions* Science 117: 528

3   Bevacqua D (2006) *Hematite formation by oxygenated groundwater at 2.76 ga and by oxygenated seawater at 3.46 ga* The Geological Society of America, Philadelphia Annual Meeting (October 2006) now published as Kato Y *et al.* (2009) *Hematite formation by oxygenated groundwater more than 2.76 billion years ago* Earth and Planetary Sciences 278:40-49 and Hoashi M *et al.* (2009) *Primary hematite formation in an oxygenated sea 3.46 billion years ago* Nature Geoscience 2: 301-6

4   http://chemistry.about.com/cs/glossary/g/bldeftetra.htm

5   Miller SL, Urey HC, Oro J (1976) Origin of organic compounds on the primitive earth and in meteorites J Mol Evol 31:59-72

6   *Biological Science* 1 and 2, 3rd edition; Cambridge University Press, page 883

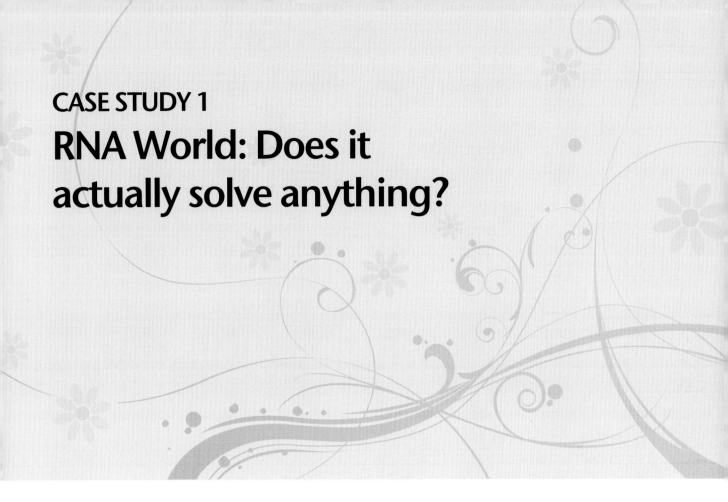

CASE STUDY 1
RNA World: Does it actually solve anything?

Living organisms are built largely of proteins but they carry specifications for their own construction in the form of DNA. When the DNA is used to specify new protein structures, hundreds of existing proteins are involved in the process of translating DNA sequences into other proteins (described in Chapter 3). This works fine so long as each new organism can inherit the essential protein machinery from a parent along with its DNA. But how did the chain of life begin? Can we say which came first: the DNA that makes proteins or the proteins that are essential to translate the information carried by that DNA?

As there is no Darwinian solution to this dilemma, alternative theories have been proposed. Probably the most widely favoured is the 'RNA world' hypothesis. This theory suggests that the earliest life forms were based on ribonucleic acid (RNA). The reasoning behind this theory is that RNA can act as a catalyst in certain biological reactions as well as carrying information. In its catalytic reactions, some of which we will consider below, RNA acts rather like a protein enzyme. Because it can perform both functions, RNA seems to present itself as an appropriate intermediate between non-living chemicals and fully-functioning DNA-based organisms.

The Structure of RNA

RNA, like DNA, is a nucleic acid. Nucleic acids are biopolymers of repeating units, each consisting of a nitrogenous base, a sugar and a phosphate group. This unit is illustrated in Figure CS1.1.

Thus, a fundamental part of RNA and DNA is a five-carbon (pentose) sugar.[1] In the

case of DNA, the sugar is called 2-deoxyribose, while in RNA it is ribose. The structures of the two sugars are shown in Figure CS1.2.

You can see from the figure that the only difference between the two sugars is the substitution of a hydrogen atom [H] for the hydroxyl group [OH] on carbon 2 of ribose.

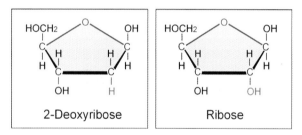

Figure CS1.1 Repeating Unit of RNA

The absence of this oxygen is the reason why this sugar (and DNA) is termed 'deoxy'.

Like amino acids, sugars can exist in two different forms, namely, "right-handed"

Figure CS1.2 Structures of 2-Deoxyribose and Ribose

(*dextro*; D) and "left-handed" (*laevo*; L), mirror images of each other. However, the sugars that are constituents of DNA and RNA are all right-handed.[2] The origin of such molecules before there were enzymes to discriminate between the two forms remains a major unresolved problem. Clearly this applies regardless of whether we are considering the prebiotic origin of DNA or that of RNA.

In 1995, the Stanley Miller group published their findings regarding the stability of ribose in a postulated prebiotic environment. They concluded:

> The existence of the RNA world, in which RNA acted as a catalyst as well as an informational macromolecule, assumes a large prebiotic source of ribose or the existence of pre-RNA molecules with backbones different from ribose-phosphate. The generally accepted prebiotic synthesis of ribose, the formose reaction, yields numerous sugars without any selectivity. Even if there were a selective synthesis of ribose, there is still the problem of stability... The ribose half-lives are very short (73 min at pH 7.0 and 100 degrees C and 44 years at pH 7.0 and 0 degrees C... These results suggest that the backbone of the first genetic material could not have contained ribose or other sugars because of their instability.[3]

Formose Reaction

The chemistry that is most often cited to explain the prebiotic synthesis of ribose is the formose reaction[4], which was discovered in 1861 by Aleksandr Butlerov. The late Professor Leslie Orgel was probably one of the most famous names in the study on how primitive life might have begun on Earth. His research focused on the nature of the chemical reactions that might have led to the origin of life. In a recent posthumous publication[5], he said:

> The only autocatalytic cycle that has been demonstrated experimentally is that involved in the formose reaction—the polymerization of formaldehyde to give a notoriously complex

mixture of products, including ribose, the organic component of the backbone of RNA... Under many circumstances, the formation of significant amounts of complex products occurs only after many hours, the time needed to complete many rounds of amplification of the impurities by means of the autocatalytic cycle... Despite some successes, it is still not possible to channel the formose reaction in such a way as to produce ribose in substantial yield.

Nevertheless, others have sought to find alternative mechanisms whereby the formose reaction could be made more efficient. For example, Lambert and co-workers have recently published a paper[6] entitled *The Silicate-Mediated Formose Reaction: Bottom-Up Synthesis of Sugar Silicates* in which they state:

> Understanding the mechanism of sugar formation and stabilization is important for constraining theories on the abiotic origin of complex biomolecules. Although previous studies have produced sugars from small molecules through the formose and related reactions, the product mixtures are complex and unstable. We have demonstrated that simple two- and three-carbon molecules (glycolaldehyde and glyceraldehyde), in the presence of aqueous sodium silicate, spontaneously form silicate complexes of four- and six-carbon sugars, respectively. Silicate selects for sugars with a specific stereochemistry and sequesters them from rapid decomposition. Given the abundance of silicate minerals, these observations suggest that formose-like reactions may provide a feasible pathway for the abiotic formation of biologically important sugars, such as ribose.

However, there is another major stumbling block to advocates of the formose reaction. Ribose is not the only component in the formation of the repeating unit of RNA and DNA. It is also necessary to have an abundant supply of the nitrogenous bases, such as adenine and cytosine. Evolutionary chemists have proposed that the nucleotide bases could possibly have been produced on the early Earth from the reaction of hydrogen cyanide with ammonium hydroxide. While this does produce small yields of adenine and other nitrogenous bases under certain conditions, this reaction also produces a variety of nitrogenous substances that completely inhibit the formose reaction. Since both the sugar and the nitrogenous bases are required for the formation of RNA, this finding creates a formidable difficulty for the RNA-world hypothesis. This problem has been highlighted by the evolutionary scientist Robert Shapiro, who states:

> The complex sugar mixture produced in the formose reaction is rapidly destroyed under the reaction conditions. Nitrogenous substances (needed for prebiotic base synthesis) would interfere with the formose reaction by reacting with formaldehyde, the intermediates, and sugar products in undesirable ways. The evidence that is currently available does not support the availability of ribose on the prebiotic earth, except perhaps for brief periods of time, in low concentration as part of a complex mixture, and under conditions unsuitable for nucleoside synthesis.[7]

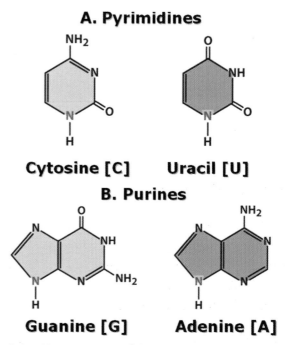

Figure CS1.3 Structures of the Four Nitrogenous Bases of RNA

The Structure of the Nitrogenous Bases of RNA

The four nitrogenous bases of RNA are shown in Figure CS1.3. There are two pyrimidines: cytosine (C) and uracil (U), and two purines: guanine (G) and adenine (A).

The only difference between DNA and RNA with respect to the four nitrogenous bases is the substitution of thymine (T) for uracil (U). The structures of these two closely-

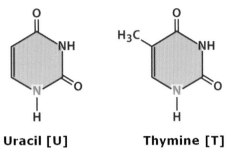

Uracil [U]　　　Thymine [T]

Figure CS1.4 Structures of Uracil and Thymine

related nitrogenous bases are shown in Figure CS1.4.

The significance of these differences will become apparent later as we discuss the significant difficulties with passing out of the postulated RNA world to the universal and current world of DNA and protein.

The prebiotic synthesis of the nitrogenous bases is fraught with difficulties. These are summarised by Shapiro:

A number of theories propose that RNA, or an RNA-like substance, played a role in the origin of life. Usually, such hypotheses presume that the Watson–Crick bases were readily available on prebiotic Earth, for spontaneous incorporation into a replicator. Cytosine, however, has not been reported in analyses of meteorites nor is it among the products of electric spark discharge experiment… To favor cytosine formation, reactant concentrations are required that are implausible in a natural setting… No reactions have been described thus far that would produce cytosine, even in a specialized local setting, at a rate sufficient to compensate for its decomposition. On the basis of this evidence, it appears quite unlikely that cytosine played a role in the origin of life.[8]

Alternative Theories for the Formation of RNA

1. Clays

Some scientists have suggested that naturally-occurring clays might provide a basis for the synthesis of RNA. We do know that clays can catalyse some chemical reactions, so some have argued that clay particles could be a suitable substrate on which important organic reactions might occur. There has even been speculation that crystal structures in the clays might be considered as 'crystal genes' to direct organic processes.[9] More recently, Ferris and co-workers have investigated the clay mineral montmorillonite.[10] They found that some samples of the mineral were effective catalysts, promoting the formation of oligomers even from dilute solutions of activated nucleotide substrates. Of course, this work assumes the availability of the activated nitrogenous bases in relatively high concentrations.

2. Life in a zinc world

In two recent theoretical publications[11], Mulkidjanian and Galperin have proposed that life may have begun on the porous surfaces of zinc sulphide deposits similar to those found today around deep sea thermal vents or 'smokers'. According to these authors, the primordial conditions would require UV-rich solar radiation and the high pressure of a carbon dioxide-dominated primeval atmosphere. They suggest that the solar radiation might drive carbon dioxide reduction, yielding the building blocks for the first biopolymers. Then the zinc sulphide deposits might act as templates for the synthesis and protection of longer biopolymers from simpler building blocks. They also suggest that the UV radiation would then have favoured the selective enrichment of photostable, RNA-like polymers. There is very little experimental evidence to support this intriguing chain of ideas.

3. Direct synthesis from mixtures of chemicals

In a recent publication in the journal *Nature*, Powner and co-workers describe the complex synthesis of some of the activated nitrogenous bases from mixtures of chemicals that they regard as plausible constituents of the prebiotic world.[12] In the abstract, they state:

> At some stage in the origin of life, an informational polymer must have arisen by purely chemical means. According to one version of the 'RNA world' hypothesis this polymer was RNA, but attempts to provide experimental support for this have failed. In particular, although there has been some success demonstrating that 'activated' ribonucleotides can polymerize to form RNA; it is far from obvious how such ribonucleotides could have formed from their constituent parts (ribose and nucleobases). Ribose is difficult to form selectively, and the addition of nucleobases to ribose is inefficient in the case of purines and does not occur at all in the case of the canonical pyrimidines. Here we show that activated pyrimidine ribonucleotides can be formed in a short sequence that bypasses free ribose and the nucleobases… The starting materials for the synthesis – cyanamide, cyanoacetylene, glycolaldehyde, glyceraldehyde and inorganic phosphate – are plausible prebiotic feedstock molecules, and the conditions of the synthesis are consistent with potential early-Earth geochemical models.

Nevertheless, Powner and his co-workers remain cautious and they conclude their paper as follows:

> Although the issue of temporally separated supplies of glycolaldehyde and glyceraldehyde remains a problem, a number of situations could have arisen that would result in the conditions of heating and progressive dehydration followed by cooling, rehydration and ultraviolet irradiation. Comparative assessment of these models is beyond the scope of this work, but it is hoped that the chemistry described here will contribute to such an assessment.[12]

This enterprising ingenuity exemplifies the creativity that is characteristic of chemical evolution research. Nevertheless, there are many evolutionary scientists who have accepted that the molecules needed to make the first living cell could never have occurred on the primeval earth, whatever the conditions and whatever the chemistry. Thus it has become scientifically respectable to look elsewhere in the cosmos for the conditions where life or its constituent parts might have arisen. These components or maybe living organisms themselves would have travelled through space on comets and meteorites.

Molecules from Outer Space

Francis Crick, the co-discoverer with James Watson of the structure of DNA, was increasingly doubtful about the possibility of life's emergence on the ancient earth. In 1973, together with Leslie Orgel, he published a paper advocating an extraterrestrial theory of origins which they called *Directed Panspermia*.[13] Furthermore, in 1993, Crick said this about the RNA world:

> It may turn out that we will eventually be able to see how this RNA world got started. At present, the gap from the primal 'soup' to the first RNA system capable of natural selection looks forbiddingly wide.[14]

More recently, Kuzicheva and Gontareva published an article entitled *Prebiotic synthesis of nucleotides at the Earth orbit in presence of Lunar soil*[15] and in support of the contention that important bio-molecules could have arisen in space, Martins *et al.* reported finding nitrogenous bases such as uracil (and xanthine) in the Murchison meteorite.[16] These authors conclude:

Some believe that important bio-molecules could have arisen in space (Photo: Andy Bluedharma/Flickr)

A continuous influx of meteoritic uracil and xanthine and possibly other nucleobases would have enriched the prebiotic organic inventory necessary for life to assemble on the early Earth. Following the birth of the Solar System, carbonaceous meteorite infall would have been common on all terrestrial planets. Consequently, nucleobases delivered to these worlds together with sugar related species and amino acids might have been beneficial to the origin of life on Earth, Mars, or elsewhere.

These four very different chemical scenarios show that there is no consensus as to how the RNA world could have arisen. This is summed up by a very recent assessment of Robertson and Joyce:

> A more tenuous argument can be made regarding whether life on Earth began with RNA. In what has been referred to as "The Molecular Biologist's Dream", one might imagine that all of the components of RNA were available in some prebiotic pool, and that these components could have assembled into replicating, evolving polynucleotides without the prior existence

of any evolved macromolecules. However, a thorough consideration of this "RNA-first" view of the origin of life inevitably triggers "The Prebiotic Chemist's Nightmare", with visions of the intractable mixtures that are obtained in experiments designed to simulate the chemistry of the primitive Earth. Perhaps this continuing nightmare will eventually have a happy ending, and recent experimental findings provide some reason for optimism. However, the problem of the origin of the RNA World is far from being solved, and it is fruitful to consider the alternative possibility that RNA was preceded by some other replicating, evolving molecule, just as DNA and proteins were preceded by RNA.[17]

The final point made by these authors has persuaded other researchers to propose and investigate alternative prebiotic scenarios. For example, Kurland has suggested the existence of a prebiotic polypeptide world in his recent paper *The RNA Dreamtime*. He writes:

> Modern cells present no signs of a putative prebiotic RNA world... Random polypeptide synthesis in a prebiotic world has the potential

to initially produce only a very small fraction of polypeptides that can fold spontaneously into catalytic domains. However, that fraction can be enriched by proteolytic activities that destroy the unfolded polypeptides and regenerate amino acids that can be recycled into polypeptides... Such open polypeptide systems may have been the precursors to the cellular ribonucleoprotein (RNP) world that evolved subsequently.[18]

The rationale behind his hypothesis is the fact that RNA rarely works as a catalyst without the involvement of protein. He speaks of ribonucleoprotein (RNP) which is a functional complex of RNA with protein(s).

RNA as a Catalyst

As we mentioned at the beginning of this case study, the initial enthusiasm for the RNA world hypothesis was triggered by the experimental finding that RNA can act as a catalyst. The catalytic activity of RNA is due to two physical characteristics. First, the molecule is flexible and can fold into three-dimensional structures. These structures are initiated and stabilised by base-pairing: adenine (A) binds preferentially to uracil (U) and guanine (G) binds preferentially to cytosine (C). This is illustrated in Figure CS1.5. Although single-stranded DNA can fold into diverse structures, it lacks the level of reactivity that would allow it to catalyse reactions.

Secondly, the main reason why RNA is more chemically reactive than DNA is the presence of the OH group on the 2' carbon (see Figure CS1.2). However, the consequence of this greater reactivity is that RNA is much less stable and more easily broken down. By contrast, the more limited chemical reactivity

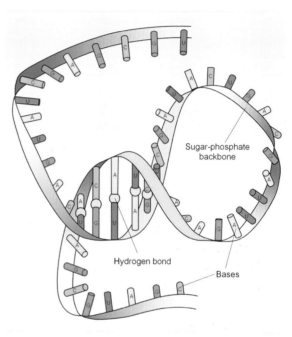

Figure CS1.5 The Folding of RNA

of DNA makes it significantly more stable and much better suited as an information storage molecule.

Ribozymes

The name 'ribozyme' is given to any RNA molecule with catalytic activity. One example of a ribozyme is in the enzyme ribonuclease P (RNase P). This enzyme creates the 5' ends of bacterial transfer RNA molecules and consists of an RNA subunit and a protein subunit, with the catalytic activity residing in the RNA. Kurland writes about this enzyme complex:

> Normally, RNase P has both RNA as well as protein components. But recently, an RNA-free variant was discovered in human mitochondria and shown to mature tRNA precursors normally. If RNase P function can be supported by protein alone, it is conceivable that such protein functions have participated in prebiotic systems as well. So, which came first, a protein or an RNP version of the enzyme?[18]

Another example of a ribozyme comes from the transcription of RNA from its DNA template, which (as we will see in Chapter 3) involves non-protein coding sequences called introns being cut out from the messenger RNA. It is possible that some introns cut themselves out by an autocatalytic process, that is, the messenger RNA acts as a ribozyme upon itself. However, this reaction generally involves the participation of many other molecules including many proteins. This complex has been called the "spliceosome" and has been considered to be "the most complex macromolecular machine in the cell".[19]

In 2003, Jurica and Moore reviewed current knowledge regarding the spliceosome and published a paper intriguingly entitled "Pre-mRNA splicing: awash in a sea of proteins".[20] They write:

> What's in a spliceosome? More than we ever imagined, according to recent reports employing proteomics techniques to analyze this multi-megadalton machine. As of 1999, around 100 splicing factors were identified; however, that number has now nearly doubled due primarily to improved purification of spliceosomes coupled with advances in mass spectrometry analyses of complex mixtures. Gratifyingly, most of the previously identified splicing factors were found in the recent mass spec studies. Nonetheless, the number of new proteins emerging with no prior connection to splicing was surprising. Without functional validation, it would be premature to label these proteins as bona fide splicing factors. Yet many were identified multiple times in complexes purified under diverse conditions or from different organisms. Another recurring theme regards the dynamic nature of spliceosomal complexes, which may be even more intricate than previously thought.

Competing with the spliceosome for the most complex molecular machinery in the cell is the ribosome, which also functions by the catalytic properties of certain RNA molecules. As we will see in Chapter 3, the ribosome is the molecular machinery that translates the information carried on messenger RNA into protein structure. It possesses many proteins and several RNA molecules such as the 23S rRNA fraction, which is involved in the formation of the peptide bond during protein synthesis.

The Structure and Function of Ribozymes

As highlighted above, Kurland et al[18] have demonstrated that the essential role of protein in the maintenance of the structure and the functioning of a ribozyme points to another chicken-and-egg situation. If the present is in any way a key to the past, RNA rarely acts as a catalyst without the involvement of protein. In addition, complementary base pairing (i.e. A binding to U and G binding to C) is vital to create the three-dimensional RNA structure without which the RNA cannot act as a catalyst. But why are these four nitrogenous bases used? A comparison of the structures of DNA and RNA is shown in Figure CS1.6

Unlike RNA, DNA is a stable double helix. It has very precise dimensions and the great achievement of Watson and Crick was the elucidation of its structure in 1953.[21] They discovered that the only nitrogenous bases that 'fit' across the helix are A (a purine) binding to T (a pyrimidine) and guanine (a purine) binding to cytidine (a pyrimidine). However, RNA is not under this physical constraint. If RNA were the antecedent to DNA, why are there just A, U, G and C in RNA? There are many other purines and pyrimidines to choose from. Why would Nature have selected these four to be the universal constituents of RNA?

The only exception to this rule appears to be transfer RNA, the adaptor molecule involved in the translation of the information carried by messenger RNA into protein structure. As we will see in Chapter 3, transfer RNA does possess some modified nitrogenous bases (e.g. methyl-guanine, methyl-adenine, dihydrouracil

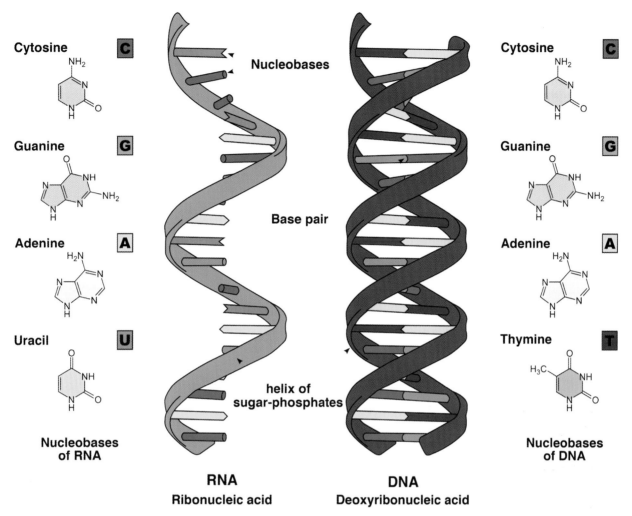

Cytosine C

Guanine G

Adenine A

Uracil U

**Nucleobases
of RNA**

Nucleobases

Base pair

**helix of
sugar-phosphates**

RNA
Ribonucleic acid

Cytosine C

Guanine G

Adenine A

Thymine T

**Nucleobases
of DNA**

DNA
Deoxyribonucleic acid

Figure CS1.6 The Structures of DNA and RNA[22]

and pseudouracil). But the exception proves the rule. These modified bases are actually synthesised from the main nitrogenous bases by complex and energetic biochemical processes.

Today, the presence of the four bases of RNA relates to the fact that this molecule is transcribed from a template of DNA which also consists of just four different nitrogenous bases (A, T, G and C). One might conclude that RNA is (and always has been) the product of DNA transcription and in no way lends itself as a precursor to life as we know it today. In fact, the information for the RNA sequence of the ribozyme is carried by the DNA and cannot be transcribed without the assistance of many proteins.

DNA is a perfect vector for the storage of biological information and can be considered as the cell's hard disk. As we have discussed,

DNA has two characteristics that make it significantly less chemically reactive but much more stable. These features include the presence of thymine for uracil and the reduction of the sugar on carbon atom 2 from a hydroxyl group to a single hydrogen atom. Both of these modifications are extremely costly in terms of chemical energy and involve complex biochemical pathways. The move away from a putative RNA world to the current world of DNA and protein has rarely been addressed in the scientific literature.

In summary, the RNA World model is the site of much creative and speculative activity in the attempt to find a coherent story for the origin of life from chemicals. For all this, the obstacles are formidable and it is increasingly difficult to believe that new breakthroughs are helping us understand what actually happened before the existence of the first living cell. With extraterrestrial theories being propounded by respected figures alongside some admissions of despair, it is clear that scepticism is as justified now as ever.

But none of this touches the next problem, which concerns the origin of biological information. We now turn to look at this in Chapter 3 and the case study which follows it.

Further Questions

1   So does the RNA World hypothesis actually solve anything?

2   Why do scientists invoke the possibility that life has come from outer space?

3   What processes are necessary for the putative RNA World to become the DNA/Protein World of today?

Case Study 1 Endnotes

1   By way of comparison, glucose is a six-carbon sugar.
2   As discussed in chapter two, the naturally occurring amino acids in proteins are all "left-handed".
3   Larralde R, Robertson MP, Miller SL (1995) *Rates of decomposition of ribose and other sugars: implications for chemical evolution* PNAS 92: 8158-60
4   Formose is a contraction of two words, namely, formaldehyde and aldose.
5   Orgel LE (2008) *The Implausibility of Metabolic Cycles on the Prebiotic Earth* PLoS Biol 6(1): e18
6   Lambert JB *et al.* (2010) *The Silicate-Mediated Formose Reaction: Bottom-Up Synthesis of Sugar Silicates* Science 327: 984-6
7   Shapiro R (1988) *Prebiotic ribose synthesis: a critical analysis* Origins of Life and Evolution of the Biosphere: Journal of the International Society for the Study of the Origin of Life 18:71-85
8   Shapiro R (1999) *Prebiotic cytosine synthesis: A critical analysis and implications for the origin of life* PNAS 96: 4396-401
9   Cairns-Smith AG (1982) *Genetic Takeover and the Mineral Origins of Life* Cambridge: University Press
10 Miyakawa S, Ferris JP (2003) *Sequence- and regioselectivity in the montmorillonite-catalyzed synthesis of RNA.* J Am Chem Soc 125: 8202–8
11 Mulkidjanian AY (2009) *On the origin of life in the Zinc world: 1. Photosynthesizing, porous edifices built of hydrothermally precipitated zinc sulfide as cradles of life on Earth* Biology Direct 2009 4:26 doi:10.1186/1745-6150-4-26; and Mulkidjanian AY and Galperin MY (2009) *On the origin of life in the Zinc world. 2. Validation of the hypothesis on the photosynthesizing zinc sulfide edifices as cradles of life on Earth* Biology Direct 2009, 4:27 doi:10.1186/1745-6150-4-27
12 Powner MW, Gerland B, Sutherland JD (2009) *Synthesis of activated pyrimidine ribonucleotides in prebiotically plausible conditions* Nature 14:239-42
13 Crick FHC, Orgel LE (1973) *Directed Panspermia* Icarus 19:341-6
14 Crick FHC (1993) The *RNA World* in Gesteland RF, Atkins JF (eds) Cold Spring Harbor Laboratory Press pp xi-xiv
15 Kuzicheva EA, Gontareva NB (2002) *Prebiotic synthesis of nucleotides at the Earth orbit in presence of Lunar soil* Adv Space Res 30:1525-31
16 Martins Z *et al.* (2008) *Extraterrestrial nucleobases in the Murchison meteorite* Earth and Planetary Science Letters 270: 130-6
17 Robertson MP, Joyce GF (2011) *The Origins of the RNA World* Cold Spring Harb Perspect Biol doi: 10.1101/cshperspect.a003608
18 Kurland CG (2010) *The RNA Dreamtime* Bioessays 32: 866–71
19 Nilsen T (2003) *The spliceosome: the most complex macromolecular machine in the cell?* Bioessays 25 (12): 1147–9
20 Jurica MS, Moore MJ (2003) *Pre-mRNA splicing: awash in a sea of proteins* Mol Cell 12:5-14
21 Watson JD, Crick FHC (1953) *A structure for deoxyribose nucleic acid* Nature 171: 737-8
22 http://commons.wikimedia.org/wiki/File:Difference_DNA_RNA-EN.svg

CHAPTER 3
Information from Molecules?

3.1 Introduction

A typical animal cell is shown in Figure 3.1. At the heart of this cell is the nucleus and, just prior to cell division, the DNA in the nucleus condenses into visible structures known as chromosomes.

In every cell, chromosomes comprise very long strands of DNA double helix "wrapped" very precisely around several kinds of proteins known as histones. These positively charged proteins are nearly identical in every living organism and any mutations to their structure tend to be fatal.

A simple diagram of the structure of the DNA double helix is shown in Figure 3.2. The two strands each comprise a sugar phosphate backbone. In the case of DNA the sugar is called deoxyribose. On the other hand, the sugar in RNA is ribose. The only difference between the two sugars, structurally, is that deoxyribose has one less oxygen atom (hence the name *deoxy*ribose). The fact that the sugar backbone contains phosphate means that it is highly negatively charged which allows the

DNA double helix to wind precisely around the positively charged histone proteins.

The two sugar phosphate backbones are held together by four nucleotide bases, which could be thought of as the rungs across the ladder. The nucleotides are complex organic molecules of two different types, purines and pyrimidines. There are two purines in DNA, namely, adenine [A] and guanine [G]. Likewise, there are two pyrimidines, namely, thymine [T] and cytosine [C]. It is not necessary to consider the structures in detail, but it should be remembered that there is only space for a purine to react with a pyrimidine across the double helix. In particular, because of hydrogen bonding constraints, adenine [A] only interacts with thymine [T] and guanine [G] only interacts with cytosine [C] across the "divide". These are the base-pairing rules for DNA.

You will remember what we said about RNA in the case study (CS1). If you look back to Figure CS1.5, you will see the structure

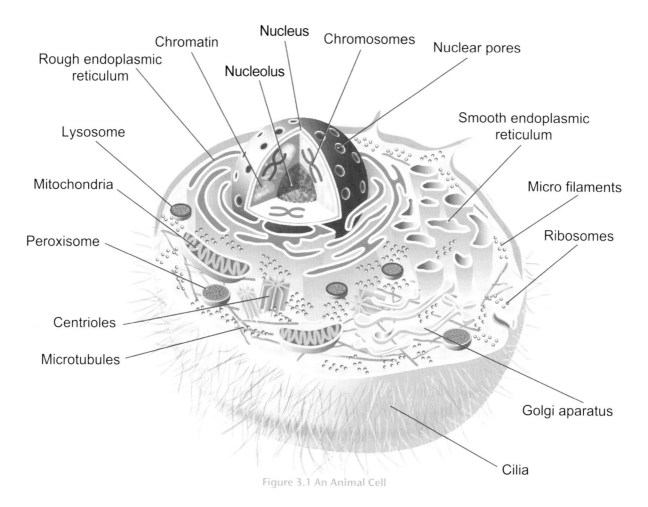

Figure 3.1 An Animal Cell

of RNA. You will notice that RNA is not a double helix like DNA because there is only a single sugar phosphate backbone. You will also notice that three of the bases are the same as DNA, namely A, G and C. However, there is no thymine [T] in RNA, which has uracil [U] instead. Chemically, this is very significant. DNA with its thymine and deoxyribose is a much more stable molecule

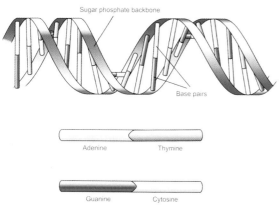

Figure 3.2 The Structure of DNA

than RNA although it is very costly in terms of biochemical energy to synthesise it. As we will see, it is vital that RNA is easily broken down. This is another reason why the "RNA world" hypothesis is difficult to accept.

The remarkable structure of the double helix was elucidated in 1953 by James Watson and Francis Crick.[1] The nature of the base pairing explained why DNA molecules could be replicated with fidelity. This is illustrated in Figure 3.3. At cell division (known as mitosis), the DNA double helix is unwound at amazing speeds with remarkable protein enzyme machinery known as helicases and topoisomerases. The two strands of the helix separate (Figure 3.3b), exposing the bases on each. Other protein machinery then constructs new complementary strands to each of the exposed parent strands (Figure 3.3c), which eventually leaves two identical daughter DNA molecules (Figure 3.3d). The base pairing rules (A binds to T and G binds to C) are an essential aspect of this replication process, ensuring that the sequence of nucleotides is preserved from parent to daughter. The replicating machinery (known as DNA polymerase) is a complex of individual proteins and possesses remarkable proof-reading capability. Because of this, mutations where one nucleotide base is substituted incorrectly are a very rare occurrence.

DNA can be likened to a genetic textbook containing all the information required to construct a living organism throughout its lifetime. A relatively small proportion of DNA, however, carries the information for all the protein machinery required for the structure and function of the organism. These DNA sequences are called protein-coding genes and carry the information for the sequence of the protein itself. The vast majority of DNA in the chromosomes, however, does not code for protein directly. Much of this non-coding DNA may be involved in the control of the expression of the protein-coding genes themselves. It is this controlled gene expression that distinguishes one cell type from another.

For example, the protein insulin (a hormone) is only produced in certain cells within the mammalian pancreas. Nevertheless, the genetic information for insulin is carried within the chromosomes of every mammalian cell. The insulin genes are only expressed in the pancreatic cells and are "switched off" in every other type of cell. Similar examples could be given for every cell type. It is easy to see that the control of gene expression is far more significant than the protein-coding process itself. The total DNA sequence in any organism is called the genome, and scientists are only now beginning to unlock its secrets. The genome may be seen as a highly dynamic information storage system, not unlike the hard disc on a computer, only far more complex.

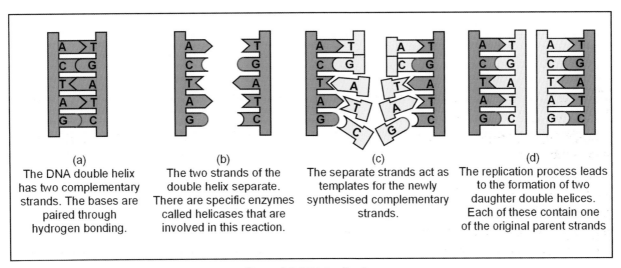

(a)	(b)	(c)	(d)
The DNA double helix has two complementary strands. The bases are paired through hydrogen bonding.	The two strands of the double helix separate. There are specific enzymes called helicases that are involved in this reaction.	The separate strands act as templates for the newly synthesised complementary strands.	The replication process leads to the formation of two daughter double helices. Each of these contain one of the original parent strands

Figure 3.3 DNA Replication

3.2 How DNA is Translated into Protein

The sequence of DNA base pairs in a protein-coding gene carries the information for the formation of the amino acid sequence of the protein. The genomic information, however, has no meaning unless it can be translated into protein structure. Accordingly, the four-letter language of DNA (A, T, G and C) has to be translated into the 20-letter language of protein. During the 1960s and 70s much research work was undertaken to elucidate this translation process.

DNA is an ideal vector for carrying biological information. The actual sequence of nucleotide bases in any one strand of the double helix is not under any biochemical constraint and can be any combination of As, Ts, Gs and Cs. The complementary strand, however, must match according to the base-

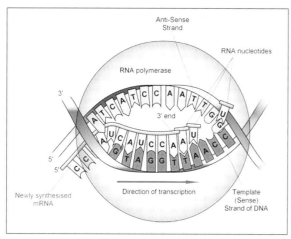

Figure 3.4 Transcription of mRNA from the DNA Template

pairing rules, where A only binds to T and G only binds to C. This means that one strand of the double helix carries the actual information for a protein, and this is sometimes called the sense or template strand. The complementary strand of the DNA is the anti-sense strand. For the translation process to begin, the double helix has to be unwound to expose the template strand. The next stage is the transcription of an intermediary molecule of messenger RNA (mRNA). This is shown in Figure 3.4.

The machinery required for transcription is a protein complex called RNA polymerase. A complementary strand of mRNA is produced based on the base-pairing rules. Thus the mRNA construct is not dissimilar to the anti-sense strand of DNA. In the mRNA, however, A now binds to U (instead of T) as G binds to C. The transcription process is under

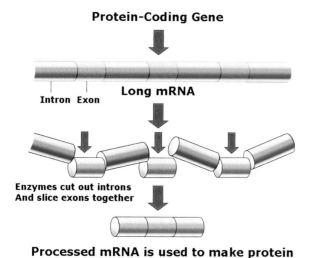

Figure 3.5 Removal of Introns

complex control. "Upstream" of the protein-coding gene are DNA sequences that facilitate the binding of the RNA polymerase and of other transcription factors which enhance or inhibit the expression of the gene. There are also start and stop signals to indicate where transcription should begin and end.

In many cases, the transcribed mRNA is modular and carries far more information than just that for the protein sequence alone. Those parts of the mRNA that code for amino acids are termed exons and those regions that do not are introns. Specific enzyme machinery cuts out the introns prior to protein synthesis. This process is illustrated in Figure 3.5.

Once the mRNA has been transcribed and processed, its sequence corresponds to the amino acid sequence of the protein. The mature mRNA is released and carried out of the nucleus of the cell to the ribosome, which is a multi-protein complex where proteins are manufactured. To translate the one type of molecule into the other, however, an adaptor is required. The adaptor molecule is another type of RNA called transfer RNA (tRNA) and its generalised structure is shown in Figure 3.6.

There are at least 64 different tRNAs although they all have the characteristic clover leaf structure, which is stabilised by intramolecular base pairing according to the RNA rules: namely, A binds to U and G binds to C. At one end of the tRNA, the so-called 3' (3 prime) end, the terminal base adenine is chemically modified so that it can bind with a specific amino acid through an ester bond.

The "bottom" of the tRNA is a sequence of three nucleotide bases called the anti-codon. This is complementary to three of the nucleotide bases within the mRNA (i.e. the codon) which codes for one of the 20 amino acids. The correspondence between codons and amino acids has been called the Genetic Code and this is shown in Figure 3.7.

As can be seen, there are 64 possible combinations of any three of the four nucleotide bases of RNA (U, A, G and C). There are, however, only 20 different amino

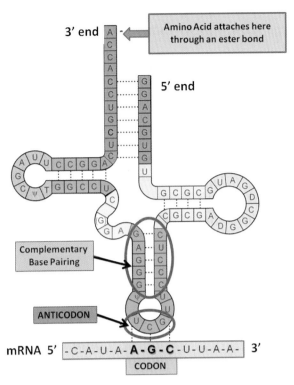

3' end

Amino Acid attaches here through an ester bond

5' end

Complementary Base Pairing

ANTICODON

mRNA 5' -C-A-U-A- **A-G-C** -U-U-A-A- 3'

CODON

Figure 3.6 Structure of tRNA

acids. Accordingly, certain amino acids have several tRNAs. For example, the amino acid leucine (Leu) has six tRNAs with six different codons, namely, UUA, UUG, CUU, CUC, CUA and CUG. On the other hand, the amino acid tryptophan (Trp) has only one (UGG). The distribution of codons is not random. The amino acids are grouped according to certain chemical characteristics. This feature of the genetic code is rarely considered in biochemistry textbooks. The design of the genetic code certainly minimises the impact of random mutation but it may also contribute another layer of biological information that is currently unknown.

We are now ready to consider the amazing process of protein synthesis performed at the ribosome. This protein "factory" complex, of which there are many thousands in each cell, comprises two major subunits. The large subunit possesses three binding sites. The

	U	C	A	G	
U	UUU] Phe UUC UUA] Leu UUG	UCU] UCC UCA] Ser UCG	UAU] Tyr UAC UAA Stop UAG Stop	UGU] Cys UGC UGA Stop UGG Trp	U C A G
C	CUU] CUC CUA] Leu CUG	CCU] CCC CCA] Pro CCG	CAU] His CAC CAA] Gln CAG	CGU] CGC CGA] Arg CGG	U C A G
A	AUU] AUC] Ile AUA AUG	ACU] ACC ACA] Thr ACG	AAU] Asn AAC AAA] Lys AAG	AGU] Ser AGC AGA] Arg AGG	U C A G
G	GUU] GUC GUA] Val GUG	GCU] GCC GCA] Ala GCG	GAU] Asp GAC GAA] Glu GAG	GGU] GGC GGA] Gly GGG	U C A G

First position (5' end)

Third position (3' end)

Amino acid names

Ala = alanine
Arg = arginine
Asn = asparagine
Asp = aspartate
Cys = cysteine

Gln = glutamine
Glu = glutamate
Gly = glycine
His = histidine
Ile = isoleucine

Leu = leucine
Lys = lysine
Met = methionine
Phe = phenylalanine
Pro = proline

Ser = serine
Thr = threonine
Trp = tryptophan
Tyr = tyrosine
Val = valine

Figure 3.7 The Genetic Code

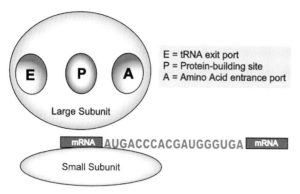

E = tRNA exit port
P = Protein-building site
A = Amino Acid entrance port

Large Subunit

mRNA AUGACCCACGAUGGGUGA mRNA

Small Subunit

Figure 3.8 The initiation of protein synthesis by the Ribosome (1)

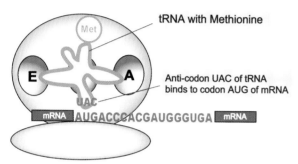

tRNA with Methionine

Anti-codon UAC of tRNA binds to codon AUG of mRNA

mRNA AUGACCCACGAUGGGUGA mRNA

Figure 3.9 The initiation of protein synthesis by the Ribosome (2)

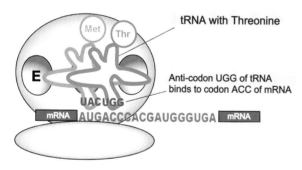

tRNA with Threonine

Anti-codon UGG of tRNA binds to codon ACC of mRNA

mRNA AUGACCCACGAUGGGUGA mRNA

Figure 3.10 The elongation phase of protein synthesis by the Ribosome (1)

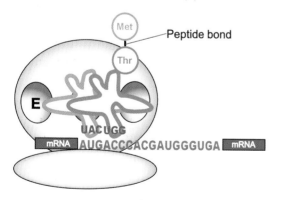

Peptide bond

mRNA AUGACCCACGAUGGGUGA mRNA

Figure 3.11 The elongation phase of protein synthesis by the Ribosome (2)

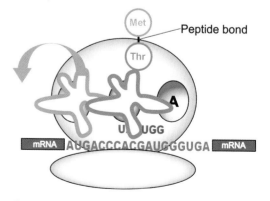

Peptide bond

mRNA AUGACCCACGAUGGGUGA mRNA

Figure 3.12 Translocation phase of protein synthesis by the Ribosome (1)

mRNA, however, first becomes associated with the smaller ribosomal subunit. This is illustrated in Figure 3.8.

At initiation of protein synthesis, the ribosomal subunits and an initiator tRNA come together at the AUG "start" codon of the mRNA. AUG actually codes for the amino acid methionine, which is always the starting amino acid in any given protein. Proteins called initiation factors are also required to bring all of these components together (see Figure 3.9).

It can be seen that the tRNA for methionine (Met) is situated in the P site of the larger ribosomal subunit. (The anti-codon of this tRNA is UAC, which is complementary to the start codon AUG in the mRNA.) During the elongation phase of protein synthesis a second tRNA moves into the A site of the ribosome. This is shown in Figure 3.10.

In this example, the second triplet codon ACC corresponds to the amino acid threonine (Thr) as shown in Figure 3.10. (The anti-codon of this tRNA is UGG, which is complementary to the codon ACC.) The ribosome also possesses its own, ribosomal, RNA (rRNA), which acts as a catalyst to create a peptide bond between the two amino acids. This is shown in Figure 3.11.

In the translocation phase the tRNA formerly in the A site is moved to the P site. This is shown in Figure 3.12.

This releases the A site to receive the next tRNA according to the next triplet codon of the mRNA and this cyclical process continues

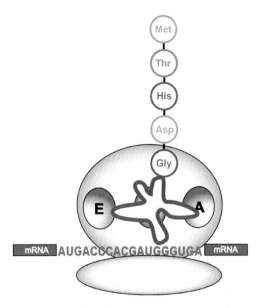

Figure 3.13 Translocation phase of protein synthesis by the Ribosome (2)

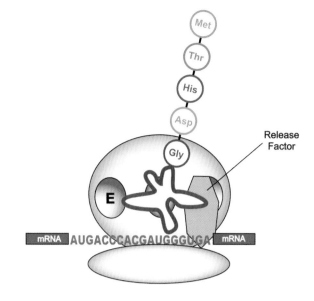

Figure 3.14 Termination phase of protein synthesis by the Ribosome (1)

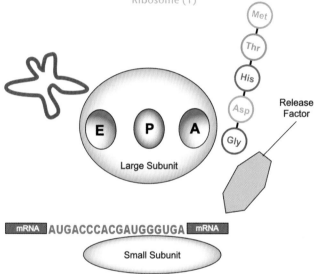

Figure 3.15 Termination phase of protein synthesis by the Ribosome (2)

until the protein is complete, as shown in Figure 3.13. Each "empty" tRNA is released from the ribosome at the E site.

The final step in protein synthesis is termination, when a "stop" codon (UGA) is encountered (see Figure 3.13). This facilitates the binding of a so-called release factor to the A site. The release factor causes the addition of a water molecule instead of an amino acid to the polypeptide chain, which then falls from the ribosome (see Figures 3.14 and 3.15).

The translation of the information carried by the mRNA is both elegant and extremely complex. Hundreds of other proteins and a great deal of chemical energy are required. For example, each of the tRNAs binds to its corresponding amino acid by the catalytic action of one of at least 64 different specific synthetase enzymes, which are themselves protein machines. In addition, there are numerous initiation, elongation and termination factors which often act as protein complexes. Furthermore, the ribosome itself is made up of many proteins (34 in the large subunit and 21 in the small subunit) as well as four different types of rRNA. The ribosome is constructed through the action of at least 200 different proteins. All the information for all these numerous proteins is carried on the DNA.

Without the protein machinery the information could not be translated, and without translation the information carried by the DNA would have no meaning. The information carried by the genes does not exist for DNA or RNA per se but for eventual protein structure. Thus the information is not contained in DNA but carried on DNA. The information itself is non-material as it has to be transcribed and translated into protein. It can be likened to the information that is being presented in this article. It is not contained in the print or the paper. The information is imparted from the mind of the author to the mind of the reader through the vector of the printed page.

3.3 The Non-Protein Coding Genome

As described previously, our DNA can be likened to the hard drive on a computer. Active protein-coding genes can be thought of as individual files and in order to extract information from the "hard disc", a copy of a "file" has to be made. This is the messenger RNA (mRNA), which can also be likened to a file copied onto a memory stick. The mRNA is free to leave the cell nucleus on its way to the ribosome "factories" where proteins are manufactured.

However, protein-coding genes only comprise a maximum of 2% of the total genome. So what about the rest? For many years, biologists believed that the remaining 98% of the genome that was not transcribed and translated into protein was non-functional. The term "junk DNA" was in common use. Times have changed.

In 2007, the first details of the ENCODE Project were published.[2] It was an unexpected finding that the vast majority of the genome was transcribed into non-protein coding RNA (ncRNA). Since 2007, this discovery has been confirmed time and time again. For example, Marcel Dinger and his colleagues at the Institute for Molecular Bioscience, University of Queensland, Brisbane published a paper in 2009 in which they state:

> Genome-wide analyses of the eukaryotic transcriptome have revealed that the majority of the genome is transcribed, producing large numbers of non-protein-coding RNAs (ncRNAs). This surprising observation challenges many assumptions about the genetic programming of higher organisms and how information is stored and organized within the genome.[3]

The word "transcriptome" has effectively replaced the obsolete term "junk DNA". This discovery has opened a window onto the unimaginable complexity of the genome. We now know that protein-coding genes only produce the "nuts and bolts" of the protein machinery of life and much (but not all) protein machinery is common between species. The ncRNAs, however, are involved in the complex regulation and time-management of gene expression and this is very different between species and also very different between the individual cells of a single organism. The non-protein coding genome comprises many distinct elements.

3.4 Introns

As shown in Figure 3.5, the initial mRNA transcript (a complementary copy of the DNA) comprises both exons and introns. However, before the mRNA is translated into protein, the introns are cut out (spliced out) of the final mRNA by specific enzymes. Whereas protein-coding RNA (i.e. without introns) comprises 2% of the human genome, intronic sequences make up approximately 25%. The functions of introns are largely unknown but scientists now recognise that the introns possess another layer of biological information that has been called the "Splicing Code". Yoseph Barash and co-workers in the Department of Electrical and Computer Engineering, University of Toronto have published a landmark paper in which they state:

> Here we describe the assembly of a 'splicing code', which uses combinations of hundreds of RNA features to predict tissue-dependent changes in alternative splicing for thousands of exons. The code determines new classes of splicing patterns, identifies distinct regulatory programs in different tissues, and identifies mutation-verified regulatory sequences. Widespread regulatory strategies are revealed, including the use of unexpectedly large combinations of features… The code detected a class of exons whose inclusion silences expression in adult tissues by activating nonsense-mediated

messenger RNA decay, but whose exclusion promotes expression during embryogenesis. The code facilitates the discovery and detailed characterization of regulated alternative splicing events on a genome-wide scale.[4]

One of the great surprises of the human genome project was the initial finding that there were only approximately 22,000 protein-coding genes. The expectation was that there would actually be hundreds of thousands. However, with the discovery of the splicing code, it is now thought that many subtly different proteins can be produced from the one RNA transcript. All of this is under highly coordinated complex control, which is different in different cells and tissues, with integrated changes throughout the lifetime of a single organism.

3.5 Pseudogenes

Pseudogenes are DNA sequences that resemble protein-coding genes but are not transcribed to messenger RNA (mRNA) in a way that could then be translated into some functional protein. Many have suggested that pseudogenes are simply molecular fossils that illustrate and provide evidence for evolutionary history. Implicit in this argument is that pseudogenes are genetic relics that have lost their original protein-coding function, which had been possessed by some ancestral creature. In support of this, evolutionary scientists point to the fact that pseudogenes are scattered throughout the genomes of all higher species (animals and plants) and, in particular, many similar pseudogenes are found in all primates.

Biologists have identified two distinct types of pseudogene, often termed "processed" and "unprocessed". This is illustrated in Figure 3.16.

In Figure 3.16, the parent protein-coding gene is depicted as having a promoter region together with exons and introns. The promoter is not transcribed (copied) into mRNA but actually controls the production of the mRNA. As mentioned above, the initial mRNA transcript (the complementary copy of the DNA[5]) comprises both exons and introns, the latter being spliced out of the final mRNA by specific enzymes (see Figure 3.5).

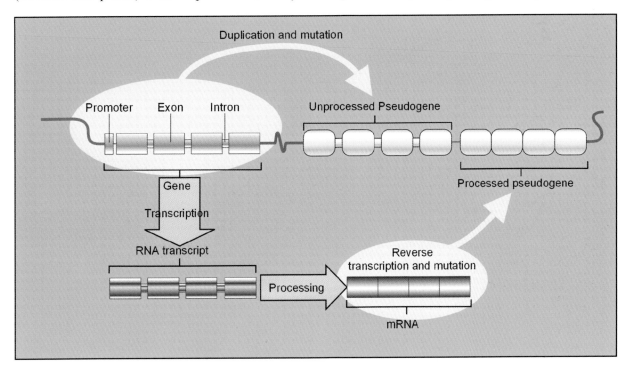

Figure 3.16 Formation of processed and unprocessed pseudogenes

As a general rule, processed pseudogenes are usually located on different chromosomes from the protein-coding genes that they resemble. Most biologists believe that they were created by the retro-transposition of the mRNA transcripts from the parent gene. This is because this type of pseudogene lacks introns. Processed pseudogenes also lack the regulatory sequences which are usually found "upstream" of protein-coding genes (before the start sequence), and they have poly-adenine (poly-A) tails[6] which are characteristic of the terminal end of an mRNA. In addition, the pseudogenes are usually flanked by repeat sequences of DNA, which is characteristic of mobile genomic elements (discussed below).

All of this evidence is very suggestive of the processed pseudogene being derived from mRNA which has been reverse transcribed back into DNA. This mechanism is somewhat similar to the incorporation of viral RNA into the host genome at specific sites characterised by regions of repetitive DNA (also discussed below).

Unprocessed pseudogenes, by contrast, are usually found in close proximity to their corresponding protein-coding gene, often on the same chromosome. As a general rule, and unlike processed pseudogenes, they do possess introns and upstream regulatory sequences. Nevertheless, it is believed that the expression of these "genes" is prevented by mutations, deletions and/or insertions of "incorrect" nucleotides. These genetic changes may lead to premature termination or may introduce "frameshifts" that render the message meaningless.

It is also suggested that unprocessed pseudogenes might arise simply by gene duplication. It is believed that the duplicated gene would be free to accumulate random mutations without actually harming the organism, which would still possess the original functional copy.

3.6 Are many Pseudogenes actually functional?

Conservation (i.e. sharing) of similar genetic sequences between species may indicate that pseudogenes (or any other non-protein coding sequence) possess important biological functions. Such sequences are said to be under purifying (or stabilising) selection, which means that deleterious mutations are removed from the gene pool and genetic diversity is restricted. This is probably the most common role of natural selection, maintaining genetic integrity (and certainly not driving evolutionary change). According to a recent review by Sasidharan and Gerstein:

> Although pseudogenes have generally been considered as evolutionary 'dead-ends', a large proportion of these sequences seem to be under some form of purifying selection - whereby natural selection eliminates deleterious mutations from the population - and genetic elements under selection have some use.[7]

Balakirev and Ayala have published two recent reviews (although one is in Russian) on the potential functions of pseudogenes.[8] In these articles, they describe examples of pseudogenes that are involved in gene expression, gene regulation and generation of genetic (antibody, antigenic, and other) diversity. In their own words:

> Pseudogenes are involved in gene conversion or recombination with functional genes. Pseudogenes exhibit evolutionary conservation of gene sequence, reduced nucleotide variability, excess synonymous over non-synonymous nucleotide polymorphism, and other features that are expected in genes or DNA sequences that have functional roles.

It was premature to suggest that pseudogenes are simply genetic fossils. This is not to say that there will never be an example of a pseudogene that is a defunct copy of a protein-coding gene which has lost its activity due to random mutational damage. But it may eventually be necessary to redefine the term "pseudogene" to distinguish between genes that are broken and those genomic elements that possess important roles in gene regulation.

3.7 Mobile Genetic Elements

The genome also contains transposable elements, or transposons. These are sequences of DNA that can move from one position in the genome to another. Transposons were discovered by Barbara McClintock, who won the Nobel Prize in 1983. There are several types of transposon and they are classified according to their mechanism of transposition.

Class I transposons are quite similar to processed pseudogenes. The DNA sequence is first transcribed into RNA and then transcribed back into DNA at another location by the enzyme reverse transcriptase. These mobile genetic elements are also called retrotransposons. Class II transposons are similar to unprocessed pseudogenes which are simply duplicated (copied) and pasted from one genomic position to another using another type of enzyme called a transposase.

Most retrotransposed genomic elements are DNA sequences known as (1) short interspersed repeated sequences (SINEs), or (2) long interspersed repeated sequences (LINEs). Both types are replicated via RNA intermediates. The majority of the SINEs are the so-called "*Alu* sequences", which are about 300 base-pairs long, and there are over one million of these in the human genome. They are so named because they can be precisely cut out of the DNA by a specific enzyme (*Alu endonuclease*) which was isolated from a bacterium (*Arthrobacter luteus*).

Nobel Prize winner Barbara McClintock (Photo: ©)

3.8 Do Alu Sequences have any function?

It is also very premature to conclude that *Alu* sequences are just "genetic fossils". Not surprisingly, there have been several recent publications that indicate that *Alu* sequences may have very important genomic roles. In 1994, Britten described the sequence analysis of 1500 interspersed *Alu* repeats of human DNA containing defined mutations.[9] He discovered that there were specific regions in the *Alu* sequence where mutations rarely occurred. Furthermore, he suggested that these highly conserved regions occurred in positions which appeared to be sites for protein binding. He concluded that:

> … the implication is that hundreds of thousands of Alu sequences have sequence-dependent functions in the genome that are selectively important for primates.

In 1997, Mighell *et al.* reviewed the then current knowledge about *Alu* sequences and their possible functions.[10] The authors described the fact that although *Alu* sequences are rare in protein-coding exons, where they would be totally disruptive, they are relatively common in introns, where they can have a dramatic impact on gene expression. In particular, normal mRNA processing which involves the removal of introns can be disrupted by point mutation in an *Alu* element, and this can lead to clinical diseases such as Alport syndrome.[11]

As a general rule, clues to the various roles for *Alu* sequences are being discovered by the identification of what goes wrong when there is a mutation or inappropriate duplication or deletion. For example, both familial hypercholesterolaemia[12] and angioedema[13] are associated with *Alu-Alu* recombinations. All of this information is circumstantial evidence that normal *Alu* sequences have important roles.

3.9 Retroviral Insertions

Retroviruses are viruses that carry their genetic material as RNA rather than DNA. They possess a relatively small number of genes and, like all viruses, cannot replicate without "hijacking" the genetic machinery of the host cell of a higher organism. Retroviruses exploit the enzyme reverse transcriptase to copy their RNA genome into DNA, which is then integrated into the host's DNA genome. From that moment on, the virus replicates as part of the host cell cycle and reproduces by transcription and translation using the cell's own machinery.

Many retroviruses are benign, but some produce disease. The classic example of a retroviral pathogen is HIV, which specifically targets cells in the immune system. Under normal circumstances, the T-cells of the immune system would be involved in eradicating a viral threat, but because they are themselves taken over by the virus AIDS has become a devastating disease. The other problem is that the structural proteins on the surface of the viral particle are constantly mutating. Consequently, it has been very difficult to come up with a universal vaccine.

It is generally assumed that these genetic insertions have entered the human genome over time and have been passed on from one generation to another. In the case of the human genome, these insertions are known as human endogenous[14] retroviruses (HERVs) and it is thought that they make up between 5% and 8% of the total genome. Most insertions have no known function, but we now understand that at least some HERVs play important roles in host biology such as the control of gene expression[15], reproduction (e.g. placental function and spermatogenesis)[16] and, indeed, enhancing resistance to infection by pathogenic retroviruses.[17]

In a landmark paper entitled *Retroviral promoters in the human genome*, Andrew Conley and co-workers at the Georgia Institute of Technology in the USA reported the existence of 51,197 HERV-derived promoter sequences that initiate transcription within the human genome.[18] These included 1,743 cases where transcription is initiated from HERV sequences that are located in gene promoter regions. In their own words:

> These data illustrate the potential of retroviral sequences to regulate human transcription on a large scale consistent with a substantial effect of ERVs on the function and evolution of the human genome.

Although this statement is couched in evolutionary language, these findings also raise the intriguing possibility that the model of an infectious viral origin of HERVs is only partly true. Is it not possible that many HERVs are actually integral functional genetic components which have, as yet, unknown function? The objection to this argument, of course, would be the similarity of the protein coding regions of the HERVs to exogenous retroviruses. However, an alternative hypothesis is that retroviruses might actually have originated as conventional genomic components that "escaped". Only time will tell if there is any substance to this tentative suggestion.

3.10 Summary

We now know that the vast majority of the genome is transcriptionally active. This is an indication of biological function but we are only just beginning to understand the complexity of biological information processing in the cell. The control of gene expression in any cell is highly complex and varies from tissue to tissue. Cellular differentiation changes over time and none of this can be haphazard. In different tissues, genes will be switched on and off. Transposable sequences may even be involved in this gene switching, with the creation of new gene sequences through the alternative splicing of mRNA transcripts.

Thus the processing of biological information is 4-dimensional, involving time. The next few years will illuminate our understanding of the complexity which is the human genome.

3.11 Further Questions

1   If biological information is not in itself material, what kinds of explanations are needed for its origin?

2   What could have come first, the Genetic Code or the protein machinery required for translating the code into protein structure?

3   Is it surprising that many proteins are very similar in structure, no matter what species possesses them?

4   Why might it be premature to consider pseudogenes as just molecular relics of an evolutionary history?

5   Why might the terms "pseudogenes" and "endogenous retroviruses" be misnomers?

Chapter 3 Endnotes

1   Watson JD, Crick FH (1953) *Molecular structure of nucleic acids; a structure for deoxyribose nucleic acid* Nature 171 (4356): 737–8.

2   Identification and analysis of functional elements in 1% of the human genome by the ENCODE pilot project. (2007) Nature 447:799-816

3   Dinger MC *et al.* (2009) *Pervasive transcription of the eukaryotic genome: functional indices and conceptual implications* Briefings in Functional Genomics 8:407-23

4   Barash Y *et al.* (2010) *Deciphering the splicing code* Nature 465:53-9

5   The mRNA is not an exact copy of the DNA. It is complementary to one of the strands of the DNA duplex (usually the sense strand). The sequence of the RNA exactly follows the base pairing rules, namely, adenine (A) in DNA will result in uracil (U) in the RNA, thymine (T) in the DNA will result in adenine (A) in the RNA, guanine (G) in DNA will result in cytosine (C) in RNA and cytosine (C) in DNA will result in guanine (G) in RNA.

6   Most processed mRNAs possess a "string" of adenine nucleotides at the end (3' end) of the message. The poly-A tail facilitates the termination of transcription and the export of the mRNA from the nucleus on its journey to the ribosome for protein synthesis. In addition, the poly-A tail protects the mRNA molecule from degradation by specific enzymes called exonucleases that are present in the cytoplasm.

7   Sasidharan R and Gerstein M (2008) *Genomics: protein fossils live on as RNA* Nature 453: 729-31.

8   Balakirev ES and Ayala FJ (2003) *Pseudogenes: are they "junk" or functional DNA?* Annu Rev Genet 37: 123-51; Balakirev ES and AyalaFJ (2004) *Pseudogenes: structure conservation, expression, and function.* Zh Obshch Biol (2004) 65:306-21.

9   Britten RJ *Evolutionary selection against change in many Alu repeat sequences interspersed through primate genomes.* Proc Natl Acad Sci USA (1994) 91:5992-6.

10   Mighell AJ, Markham AF and Robinson PA (1997) *Alu sequences.* FEBS Lett 417:1-5.

11   Knebelmann B *et al.* (1995) *Splice-mediated insertion of an Alu sequence in the COL4A3 mRNA causing autosomal recessive Alport syndrome.* Hum Mol Genet 4:675-9

12   Lehrman MA *et al.* (1987) *Duplication of seven exons in LDL receptor gene caused by Alu-Alu recombination in a subject with familial hypercholesterolemia.* Cell 48:827-35

13   Ariga T, Carter PE and Davis AE 3rd(1990) *Recombinations between Alu repeat sequences that result in partial deletions within the C1 inhibitor gene.* Genomics 8:607-13

14   "Endogenous" means that they come from within the genome, in contrast with exogenous retroviral sequences, which have been inserted from elsewhere by (exogenous) retroviruses during the life of the individual.

15   Sin HS *et al.*(2006) *Transcriptional control of the HERV-H LTR element of the GSDML gene in human tissues and cancer cells.* Arch Virol 151:1985-94

16   Muir A, Lever A and Moffett A (2004) *Expression and functions of human endogenous retroviruses in the placenta: an update.* Placenta 25 Suppl A: S16-25; Larsson E, Andersson AC, Nilsson BO (1994) *Expression of an endogenous retrovirus (ERV3 HERV-R) in human reproductive and embryonic tissues -evidence for a function for envelope gene products.* Ups J Med Sci 99:113-20

17   Ponferrada VG, Mauck BS, Wooley DP (2003) *The envelope glycoprotein of human endogenous retrovirus HERV-W induces cellular resistance to spleen necrosis virus.* Arch Virol 148:659-75

18   Conley AB, Piriyapongsa J, Jordan IK (2008) *Retroviral promoters in the human genome.* Bioinformatics 24:1563-7

Molecules packed with Information: Just what is it?

As has been explained in the main text, biological information is essentially non-material. The protein-coding part of the DNA in living systems functions according to the order of the nucleotide bases. A triplet of these (see Figure CS2.1) codes for a particular amino acid, and the whole sequence is then translated into a protein which comprises part of the machinery in all living creatures.

Information Transcends the Biochemistry

The important point to recognise is that it is not the biochemistry of the system that determines the code used in DNA. First, the Genetic Code states (for example – see Figure CS2.1) that the sequence cytosine (C), adenine (A) and thymine (T) in the DNA represents a particular amino acid (histidine) in a protein. The Code is thus a language whereby the coding string of a section of the DNA in the nucleus of the cell has exactly the same meaning as the mRNA (except that uracil in mRNA replaces thymine in DNA). This allows the information from the DNA to be used by the single stranded mRNA. Codon triplets of nucleotides cause the ribosome to gather a particular amino acid. The meaning of the codon triplet derives from that stored by the DNA, and causes the correct sequence of amino acids to be constructed (and thus the correct protein) as the final product of transcription. Essentially, this is very similar to the function of software in a digital computer. Information is stored in the arrangement of letters using a code that is not defined by the hardware itself (whether it is the chemical letters in living systems or the bits of stored electric charge representing 1 or 0 in man-made computer memory chips). So the coded 'word' is not defined by the chemicals themselves. One could not fill in the Genetic Code table given in Figure 3.7 just from knowledge of chemistry or physics. This is a very important issue which has been discussed in detail by Gitt.[1] His seminal work

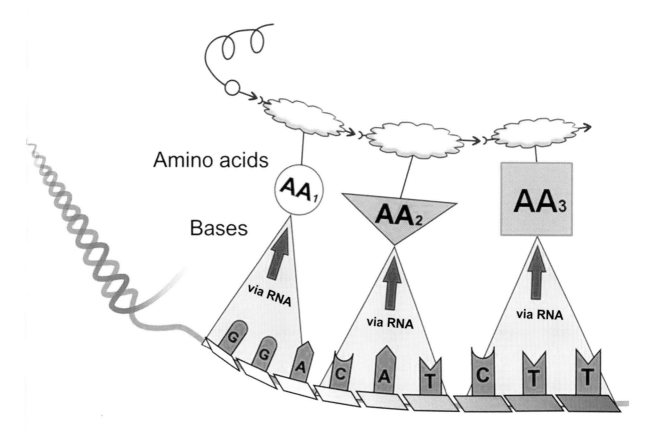

Three bases code for one amino acid

Figure CS2.1: Each triplet of nucleotides codes for an amino acid

shows that information gain or loss cannot be measured in terms of the chemistry since the code used in the message transfer, though requiring a material transfer agent (the nucleotides and mRNA etc.), is not defined by the transfer agent itself.

However there is a deeper issue which also emerges. Just as the code language is not defined by the material transfer agent, neither is the message itself defined by the code (or by its material medium). This is a more subtle issue, so an illustration might help. This article is written in English, but could be translated into French. The alphabet would be essentially the same but the French "code" is a completely different way of using the letters. So the first point is that the code (or language) is not defined by the letters themselves just as a French-English dictionary cannot be deduced from the nature of the printed letters. The second point is that the same message can be written in totally different languages, and

knowing a language does not allow someone to predict the contents of this article without reading it. This is obvious, but the implication is that the message is transcendent to the coded structure (the print on this page) and to the code itself (e.g. English or French). Again, Gitt[1] shows fundamentally that gain or loss of genetic information cannot be measured in terms of chemistry, since neither the code nor the messages are material entities.

So what is the origin of information? We have seen that it cannot be derived from the material medium, or from the code itself. Indeed, since information is non-material, its origins can never be properly explained in material terms. When one wants to explain coded structures, it is necessary to infer intelligence behind the code, and thus a mind which has invented both the code and the message and has put them together. The Rosetta stone, discovered by Bouchard in 1799 in Egypt, had a message in hieroglyphics which was also in Demotic and

Greek. This enabled Champollion to decipher the Egyptian hieroglyphics and thus unlock all messages written in other places in this ancient picture language. That principle illustrates the fundamental principle that a message is not defined by a code but is transcendent to it.

Three Views of Informational Reality

How one views reality (ontology) is actually foundational to how one then considers the evidence of the presence of information in living systems. The philosophical basis from which a person approaches his or her investigations largely governs the way genetic information is understood. The following is a summary of the way people interpret the evidence concerning information in living systems:

a) Reductionist approach

Matter and energy is all there is. This is the materialistic view of information, and it supposes that all complex functional systems, including information systems, emerge by natural selection of randomly-varying, self-replicating entities. This view[2] is espoused by Professors Richard Dawkins (Oxford University), Steve Jones (University College London) and Peter Atkins (Oxford University). Their approach is on the basis of atheism, and not surprisingly concludes that non-material information and design are an illusion when it comes to their scientific investigations. However, as Truman[3] has shown in response to the view of Dawkins, biological systems function precisely because information is present and not the reverse. That is, biological systems have not made or developed their own software.

b) 'Bottom up' approach

Information is non-material but has arisen out of matter and energy. In this view it is suggested this has happened due to areas of low entropy forming in non-equilibrium systems. This is the view that was held by Ilya Prigogine (1917-2003), and is furthered today in the writings of Yockey[4] (University of California at Berkeley)

Richard Dawkins is renowned for his reductionist view of reality (Photo: Mark Coggins/Flickr)

and Wicken[5] (Pennsylvania State University). These writers are not closed to the idea of non-material entities having meaning. Roger Penrose (Oxford), who wrote the book *The Emperor's New Mind*[6], similarly claims that mathematics is a profound demonstration of the logical principles behind the Universe and even ascribes an 'existence' to them.

In the 'bottom up' approach, if a low entropy location in the Universe (or multiverse) could be located in space-time, then it is suggested that information would emerge.

This view is held by the majority of scientists working in the field of thermodynamics of living systems, but experimental evidence does not support the notion that non-equilibrium thermodynamics can produce information on its own. A sustained region of low entropy, even in non-equilibrium conditions, does not of itself equate with a meaningful arrangement of material into a coded syntax such as is necessary in information systems. Energy and mass flow (such as in an open thermodynamic system), condensation and crystallisation do not of themselves produce new coded instructions, though such processes can modify (usually deleteriously) what is already there.

c) 'Top down' approach

Information constrains the thermodynamics of the local matter and energy via 'top-down' levels of information exchange (Gitt[1]). In this approach the idea of meaning and nonmaterial information is the philosophical starting point. The encoded systems derive from intelligence. Rather than machines building their own information systems (options a) and b) above), non-material coded instructions (information) constrain the machinery to operate in accordance with these coded instructions.

Gitt[1] has shown that information transfer needs to be analysed at several levels involving language (syntax/code) and semantics (meaning). This approach[7,8,9,10,11] leads to the proposition that machinery and information are closely intertwined in living systems. Thermodynamic considerations[7,8] show that the positive free-energy bonds involved in such intricate machinery as DNA, RNA and the ATP motor cannot arise spontaneously since the change required in free energy is positive. A random flow of energy will not achieve this. Rather than nucleotide machinery making the DNA code and the information transfer system using RNA, the reverse is, in fact, the case.

Gaylord Simpson and Beck[12] wrote:

In the face of the universal tendency for order to be lost, the complex organization of the living organism can be maintained only if work – involving the expenditure of energy – is performed to conserve the order. The organism is constantly adjusting, repairing, replacing, and this requires energy. But the preservation of the complex, improbable organization of the living creature needs more than energy for the work. It calls for information or instructions on how the energy should be expended to maintain the improbable organization.

The information placed in living systems orders the matter and energy involved in the sugar phosphate and nucleotide bonds of the DNA. Non-material information (coded arrangements) ensures that the DNA polymerase which manufactures DNA performs its task in the highly non-equilibrium biochemical environment of the living cell. It is the information (non-material, but expressed as arrangements of nucleotide triplets) which determines the biochemistry.

Furthermore, recent research has confirmed that the non-coding parts of DNA previously thought to be "junk DNA" are in fact not to be regarded as such.[13] More research is now coming to light[14] showing that the very folding patterns of proteins constitute a separate form of information transfer (implying multiple levels of information in the genome). This complex intertwining of information and matter lies at the heart of life itself, and is fundamentally changing how we understand living systems.

It is non-material information which constrains matter and energy – not information arising out of some chemical pre-history. Matter and energy cannot of themselves produce more information than that which is inherently there beforehand. This issue concerning how information and thermodynamics interconnect strikes right at the heart of the current scientific debate on origins.

Further Questions

1   What fundamentally is information?

2   Is information defined by the chemicals used in the DNA and other cellular structures?

3   Can information ever arise without intelligence?

4   Using the analogy of software and hardware in a computer, what would the equivalent be for communication systems in the cell?

Case Study 2 Endnotes

1   Gitt W (1989) *Information: the third fundamental quantity* Siemens Review 56:36-41

2   Dawkins R (2003) *The Information Challenge* 107-122 (quote is from pp. 120-121), Chapter 2.3 of *A Devil's Chaplain: Selected Essays* by Richard Dawkins (Ed) Latha Menon Phoenix. In this chapter he considers Shannon's theory of information - this theory is an important theory for assessing how much potential information can be carried in a system, but ignores the nature and source of the information. The difference is vital – best illustrated by the information-carrying capacity of a DVD and that which it actually contains.

3   Truman R (1999) *The problem of information for the theory of evolution - has Dawkins really solved it?* http://www.trueorigin.org/dawkinfo.asp (accessed January 2010)

4   Yockey H (1992) *Information theory and molecular biology* Cambridge University Press

5   Wicken JS (1987) *Evolution, Thermodynamics, and Information: Extending the Darwinian Program* Oxford University Press

6   Penrose R (1989) *The Emperor's New Mind* Oxford University Press

7   McIntosh AC (2006) *Functional Information and Entropy in living systems* In: Design and Nature III: Comparing Design in Nature with Science and Engineering Vol 87 of WIT Transactions on Ecology and the Environment Brebbia CA (ed.) WIT Press pp. 115-26

8   McIntosh AC (2009) *Information and Entropy: Top-down or bottom-up development in living systems?* International Journal of Design and Nature 4:4 351-85

9   Trevors JT, Abel DL (2004) *Chance and necessity do not explain the origin of life* Cell Biology International 28:729-39

10   Trevors JT, Abel DL (2006) *Self-organization vs. self-ordering events in life-origin models* Physics of Life Reviews 3:211–28

11   Abel DL (2009) *The Capabilities of Chaos and Complexity* Int J Mol Sci 10:247-91

12   Simpson GG, Beck WS (1965) *Life: An Introduction to Biology* 2nd ed London: Routledge, Kegan, Paul London 145

13   Birney E *et al.* (2007) *Identification and analysis of functional elements in 1% of the human genome by the ENCODE pilot project* Nature 447:799-816

14   Tramontano A (2005) *The ten most wanted solutions in protein bioinformatics* Chapman and Hall. See particularly chapter 4 *Problem 4: Protein Structure Prediction* pp. 69-88

Chapter 4
Complexity from Simplicity?

4.1 The Fossil Record

The fossil record is one of the most common sets of evidence given for macroevolution. It is named as such in the UK National Curriculum for Key Stage 4 Science, and so features in most syllabuses and textbooks at this level and above.

But there are several facts about the fossil record which do not fit well with Darwin's theory of evolution and its modern synthesis – facts which evolutionists need to explain rather than use as evidence for the theory. Charles Darwin was very aware of this in his day and devoted a whole chapter of *The Origin of Species* to the subject.

The key problem is this: Darwin's theory relies on minute changes in organisms which slowly accumulate, gradually changing the organism until it eventually becomes a new species. If this is correct, then the fossil record should show a continuum of forms suggesting evolutionary pathways between different species. But this is not what the fossil record shows. As Darwin put it:

Geology assuredly does not reveal any such finely-graduated organic chain; and this, perhaps, is the most obvious and serious objection which can be urged against the theory.[1]

How did Darwin overcome this "obvious and serious objection"? He claimed that the gaps were due to "the extreme imperfection of the geological record" – the fossil record does not in fact give a very good record of the past. One justification for this at the time was the still very limited knowledge of the global fossil record. Darwin expected more "fine gradations" to be found as research continued.

But when, 140 years later, Professor Steve Jones of University College London published an updated version of Darwin's *Origin of Species* in 1999, the fossil record still posed the same problem.

The fossil record - in defiance of Darwin's whole idea of gradual change - often makes great leaps from one form to the next. Far from the display

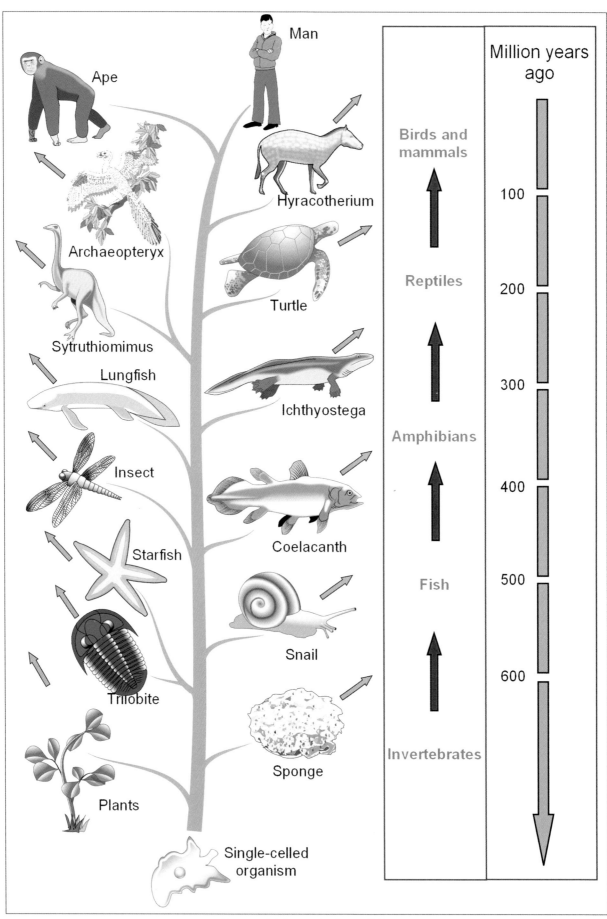

Figure 4.1 A Darwinian Tree of Life

of intermediates to be expected from slow advance through natural selection many species appear without warning, persist in fixed form and disappear, leaving no descendants. Geology assuredly does not reveal any finely graduated organic chain, and this is the most obvious and gravest objection which can be urged against the theory of evolution.[2]

In other words, the fossil record doesn't give a picture like the flowing tree shown in Figure 4.1.

The fossil record is a topic of ongoing debate among evolutionary biologists. On one side, geneticists and theoreticians stand for Darwinian "gradualism." They continue to claim that the lack of intermediate forms is due to the rarity of fossilisation and the resulting imperfection of the fossil record. In this view, the fossil record is something which needs to be explained – it is not good evidence for Darwinian evolution.

On the other side, many of those with a more first-hand knowledge of fossils stand for "punctuated equilibrium": evolution occurs mainly in sudden bursts, with long periods of little change. This explains why more intermediate forms are not found. They were around for such relatively short times that the chance of their being fossilised was very low. However, punctuated equilibrium lacks a clear mechanism. How was biological change produced as fast as the fossil record seems to require? This is still debated.

This has led some scientists to suggest that both evolutionist explanations are wrong, and

that all life has not evolved from a common ancestor. Intermediate forms are not found in the fossil record because they have never existed. In the view of these scientists, unlike that of evolutionists, the fossil record is a very good source of evidence about past organisms.

Non-evolutionists agree with one another that the fossil record is an accurate portrayal of species in the past, and that intermediate forms never existed. But they disagree on the dating of the fossil record. Some accept the conventional dating of millions of years, and propose some sort of intelligent intervention at different moments throughout geological history to modify or create organisms. Others propose that all organisms were created at one time, and that the fossil record provides snapshots, reflecting results of speciation, extinctions and ecological zonation at the times of catastrophic events.

So, rather than being straightforward evidence for evolution, the fossil record is the subject of a great deal of scientific controversy.

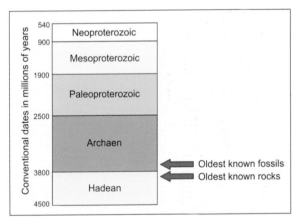

Figure 4.2 Conventional Dating of the Pre-Cambrian

4.2 Life in the Pre-Cambrian

Fossil evidence and comparisons of modern organisms suggest that life was present soon after the earth was hospitable. One potential example of ancient fossils is found in ancient rocks that resemble modern stromatolites. Electron microscopy has revealed structures that resemble modern photosynthetic cyanobacteria. According to J. William Schopf of the University of California:

Among the oldest of these putatively microfossiliferous units is a brecciated chert of the 3465 Ma Apex Basalt of Western Australia... Such data, together with the presence of stromatolites, microfossils, and carbon isotopic evidence of biological activity in similarly aged deposits, indicate that the antiquity of life on Earth extends to at least 3500 Ma.[3]

Figure 4.3 Australian Stromatolites (Photo: iStock) and Fossil Cyanobacteria

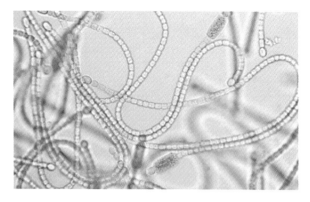

Figure 4.4 Living Cyanobacteria (Photo: iStock)

According to conventional dating methods, this is only two to three hundred million years after the cooling of the earth's crust and the oldest known volcanic (igneous) rock (see Figure 4.2). This is a blink of an eye in terms of accepted evolutionary timescales.

Modern and ancient stromatolites are colonies of photosynthetic cyanobacteria (see Figures 4.3 and 4.4). These colonies capture light from the sun and utilise this energy to fix atmospheric carbon dioxide into carbohydrates (sugar and starch), which in turn are substrates for the biosynthesis of fatty acids, amino acids and nucleotide bases, the units of lipids, proteins and nucleic acids (e.g. DNA and RNA) respectively.

4.3 Photosynthesis

Photosynthesis is a very complex biochemical process in two stages. The first stage is the light reaction which converts the direct energy from light into chemical energy in the form of adenosine triphosphate [ATP], which can be used in the biosynthesis of carbohydrates in the second stage or dark reaction. This is illustrated in Figure 4.5

In the light reaction, specific wavelengths of light are absorbed by the green pigment chlorophyll. This energy (photons) excites chlorophyll's electrons to a higher energetic state. The structure and absorption of chlorophyll is shown in Figure 4.6.

Chlorophyll is a complex organic molecule. At the heart of its light capturing mechanism is a magnesium ion [Mg] which is held in place by a complex arrangement of nitrogen atoms. It is a stable arrangement, precisely balanced to allow the excitation of electrons. However, without precise coordination with other molecules, the excitation of chlorophyll's electrons would simply be lost as heat and light (fluorescence).

Furthermore, photons are initially "grabbed" (absorbed) by other pigments and their energy is passed on to the chlorophyll reaction centre. The highly energised electrons are then passed stepwise to other specialised molecules in close proximity, forming an electron transfer chain. Eventually, electrons are "returned" to the reaction centre by "tearing them" out of water molecules resulting in the liberation of oxygen and hydrogen ions (protons).

The energy of the electrons is progressively lost as they proceed through this highly coordinated transfer system. This energy is not wasted but "trapped" as chemical energy in the form of several complex molecules, the most common of which is ATP. In this case, the liberation of energy during the progress of electrons through the transfer chain is used to add inorganic phosphate [Pi] to adenosine diphosphate [ADP] to create the high energy phosphate bond of ATP. This energy can then be used in subsequent biosynthetic pathways. The overall process is known as photosystem II, as illustrated in Figure 4.7.

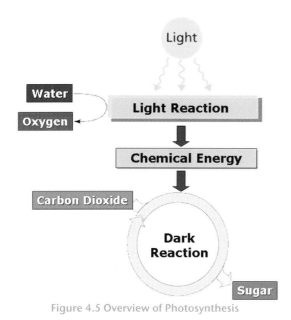

Figure 4.5 Overview of Photosynthesis

It can be seen that this photosystem comprises many complex molecules (including the proteins of the electron transfer chain) which have to be present, specifically arranged and correctly aligned with one another in order for the light-harvesting process to proceed. Many bacteria have only this one photosystem. Cyanobacteria (as well as higher plants), however, also have another photosystem, called photosystem I, which uses another form of chlorophyll absorbing slightly different wavelengths of light. The movement of electrons through photosystem I results in the formation of hydrogen-donating molecules such as NADPH, which are used for biosynthesis.

4.4 The Dark Reaction

The chemical energy and hydrogen-donating molecules produced during the light reactions of photosynthesis are used in the formation of carbohydrates during the so-called dark reaction. An important stage in this biosynthetic pathway is the fixation of carbon dioxide by the enzyme Ribulose-1,5-bisphosphate carboxylase, commonly known as RuBisCo. This enzyme is so named because its substrate is ribulose-1,5-bisphosphate. The product formed following the fixation of carbon dioxide is a highly

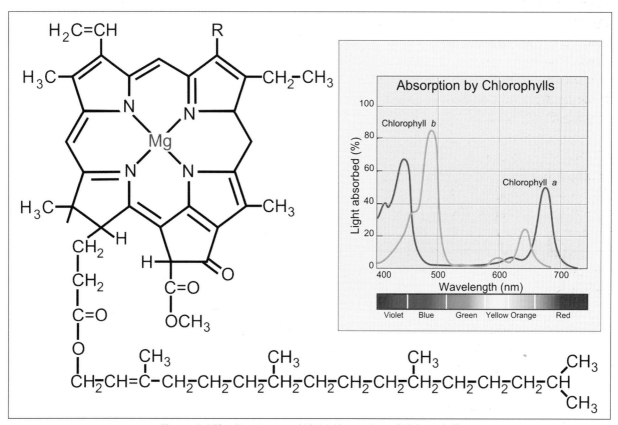

Figure 4.6 The Structure and Light Absorption of Chlorophyll

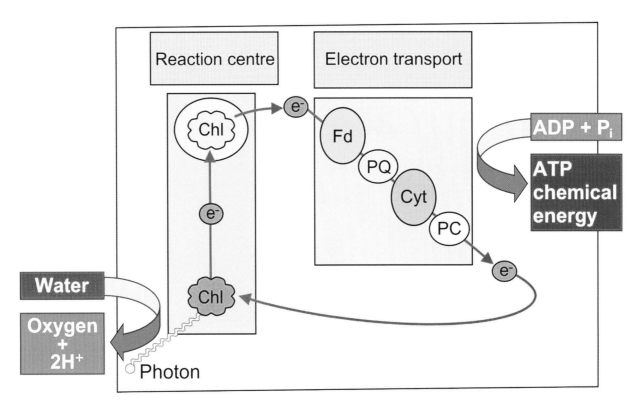

Figure 4.7 Movement of Electrons and Production of Chemical Energy by Photosystem II

unstable intermediate, which decays virtually instantaneously to form two molecules of 3-phosphoglycerate, which are then used to make glucose using chemical energy from ATP and energetic hydrogen donation from NADPH. The overall reaction (known as the Calvin Cycle after its discoverer) is shown in Figure 4.8.

RuBisCo is thought to be the most abundant protein in the world and is very important since it catalyses the chemical reaction which introduces inorganic carbon into the biosphere. The enzyme has eight large and eight small protein subunits forming a complex with a molecular weight of approximately half a million. Magnesium ions are also needed for enzymatic activity.

4.5 The Significance of Photosynthesis by Cyanobacteria

We are now in a position to consider the implications of photosynthesis by cyanobacteria, which are generally regarded by evolutionary biologists as the most ancient organisms on earth. It is believed that it was the emergence of the cyanobacteria which transformed the primordial atmosphere by addition of vast quantities of oxygen. We have already considered the fact that a non-oxygenated atmosphere is assumed because the presence of oxygen makes theories of chemical evolution very difficult.

However, there are significant problems that are rarely considered. In particular, there can be no life at all without fully functional photosynthesis. The fact is that no-one disputes the suggestion that cyanobacteria were abundant on earth relatively shortly after the cooling of the earth's crust. This is very little time at all in evolutionary terms. The rapid emergence of fully operational photosystems presents an insurmountable difficulty for Darwinism. Each individual component - whether it be chlorophyll, other pigments or all the proteins involved in electron transport - simply cannot generate chemical energy or any hydrogen-donating molecule independently. They all work in

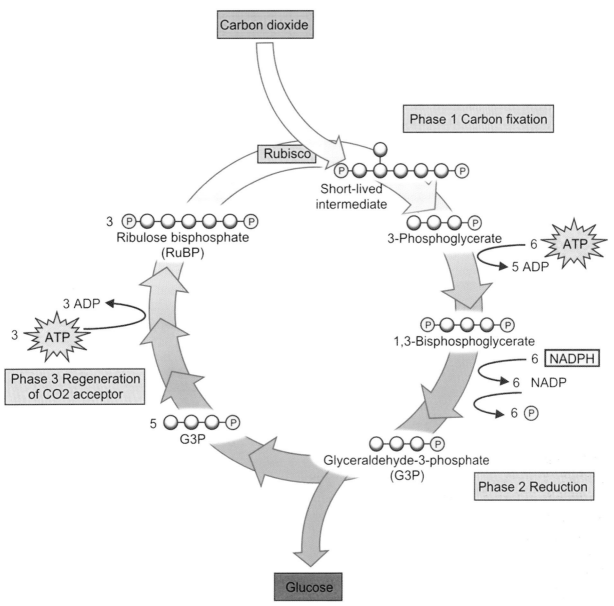

Figure 4.8 Dark Reactions of Photosynthesis

tandem in a highly ordered process.

Furthermore, chemical energy per se is redundant unless there are the complex biosynthetic pathways with all the necessary enzyme machinery present for the formation of complex biological molecules such as carbohydrates, lipids, proteins (including those same biosynthetic enzymes) and nucleic acids (e.g. DNA and RNA).

4.6 Further Questions

1   How would you decide whether an important transitional form is really missing from the fossil record?

2   The fossil record cannot be expected to preserve every step of an evolutionary pathway that we would ideally like to see. So how can we decide whether or not a given set of fossils provides good evidence for gradualistic evolution?

3   What are the problems with believing that the fossil record is so poor that transitional forms were not fossilised just by chance?

4   What are the problems with believing that evolution took place so quickly that transitional forms were not around for long enough to be fossilised?

5   It is generally accepted that cyanobacteria are ancient organisms appearing shortly (in evolutionary terms) after the earth became hospitable. What biochemical difficulties need to be overcome for this to occur?

6   It is generally believed that the action of cyanobacteria transformed the earliest atmosphere by the liberation of vast quantities of oxygen. If this is true, what can we say about oxygen toxicity?

7   What needs to be in place in order for carbon dioxide and light to be transformed into sugar?

Chapter 4 Endnotes

1   Darwin C (1859) *On the Origin of Species* page 227
2   Jones S (1999) *Almost Like a Whale* Doubleday page 252
3   Schopf JW *et al.* (2007) *Evidence of Archean life: Stromatolites and microfossils* Precambrian Research 158:141-155

CASE STUDY 3
Radiometric Dating: Just how certain is it?

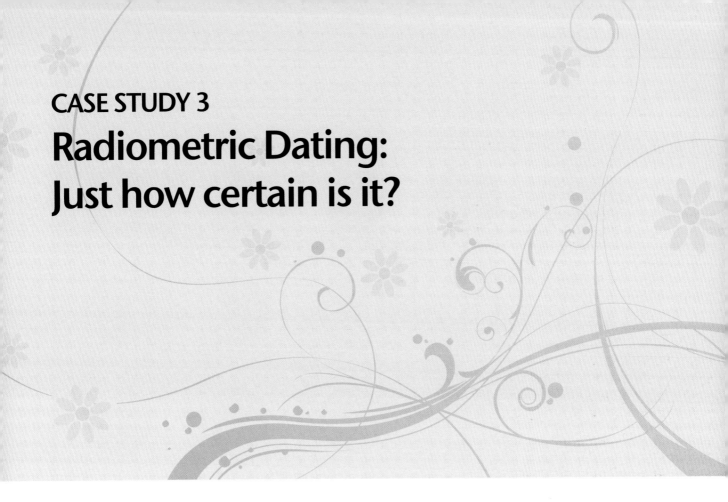

For large-scale evolution to have taken place, enormous lengths of time are necessary. Evolutionary processes are said to have occurred over millions, and in some cases, billions of years. Documented human history goes back only several thousands of years BC. A case for long ages has been made by considering the formation of sedimentary rock layers in the geological column, and, in effect, by assuming that the evolutionary scenario of change over long timescales is true. However, it is now well known that deposition of sedimentary rock layers, that is rock laid down as sediment in moving fluids such as water, can occur very rapidly, even in hours or days, given the right (catastrophic) conditions.

> The hurricane, the flood or tsunami may do more in an hour or a day than the ordinary processes of nature have achieved in a thousand years. In other words, the history of any one part of the earth, like the life of a soldier, consists of long periods of boredom and short periods of terror.[1]

Many of the world's rock layers are sedimentary in nature, such as limestone, sandstone, shale etc. These cannot easily be dated using radioisotope schemes, although some methods have been proposed and are applied. Many people have the mistaken idea that carbon dating provides evidence for millions of years. However, the ^{14}C method is only valid for ages less than 100,000 years. This is because the half-life of ^{14}C (5730 years) is such that after 10 or so half lives the amount of ^{14}C is undetectable on all but the most sensitive mass spectrometers. It is therefore safe to say that if there is any measured ^{14}C then this is evidence that the sample cannot be millions of years old.[2] ^{14}C dating was used to establish that scientific fraud had occurred in the case of Piltdown man.[3] It is usually through radiometric dating of igneous and metamorphic rocks that long ages (>1 million years) are inferred. Igneous rocks (e.g. basalts) were once very hot and have now cooled. Such rock layers have been dated using other radiometric methods and many believe that this provides the strongest evidence for a multi-billion-year-old earth.

The Uranium-Lead Method

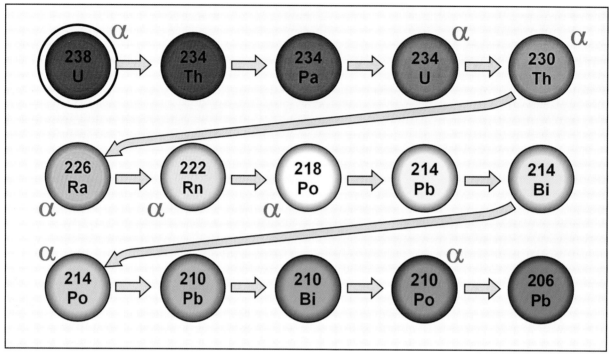

Figure CS3.1 U238 Decay Series

The first radiometric technique which was well studied was the uranium-lead method and this forms the basis for all the later techniques. This method uses the fact that radioactive uranium-238 decays spontaneously to lead-206 through a series of intermediate isotopes (see Figure CS3.1). The uranium (U) is termed the parent and lead (Pb) the daughter isotope. The rate at which parent ^{238}U decays to the daughter ^{206}Pb is accurately measurable and is termed the half-life, which may be defined as the time it takes for half of a given number of U atoms to decay into Pb atoms.

Using mass spectrometry techniques it is also possible to determine extremely accurately the amount of U and Pb present in a given rock sample. It is important to realise, however, that the error bars associated with a given date (e.g. 800 ± 20 million years) reflect the accuracy of isotope ratio determination, not the uncertainty in the age of the rock. The data actually measured are (a) the amount of the different isotopes present in the rock sample and (b) the current rate of decay under the laboratory conditions in operation at the time of the measurement. To infer the age of the rock from the measured data requires at least three assumptions. As with any scientific technique it is essential to examine the underlying assumptions. These govern the interpretation of the results and hence the conclusions obtained.

Assumptions Underlying Radiometric Dating

The three main assumptions underlying radiometric dating are:

1. There has been no loss (or gain) of parent or daughter isotope over the lifetime of the rock except by radioactive decay (i.e. the rock forms a closed system).

2. The amount of the daughter isotope present at the start of the period being dated is known with certainty.

3. The measured rate of decay (half-life) has been constant over the period being dated.

The first assumption, that of a closed system, assumes that neither the parent nor daughter concentrations (nor any of the intermediate products) have been altered throughout the entire history of the rock, apart from by radioactive decay. This is a huge assumption given the inferred timescale involved (millions or even billions of years). Furthermore, as we go back in time the assumption of closure becomes less rather than more likely. In the case of U-Pb one of the intermediate products (radon) is a mobile gas, loss of which will introduce an error in the inferred age. Furthermore, uranium and some of its decay products are soluble in water to varying degrees. If any of the isotopes occurring early in the chain shown in Figure CS3.1 (e.g. U or Th) were to be removed by groundwater contamination (a process known as "leaching") then the age of rock inferred would be much greater than its actual age. Open system behaviour is well known and documented. In the geological literature there are examples where previously published dates have been rejected in later studies for this very reason.

The second assumption is usually even more difficult to guarantee than the first, and represents the greatest problem with the technique. If some of the daughter isotope was already present at time zero (i.e. when the rock was formed) then the age of the rock will appear older than it actually is. Even a newly formed rock would have an appearance of age. A good example of this is found in dating studies of rock from Sunset Crater in Arizona. Tree ring dating gave the date of the volcanic eruption that created this crater at about AD 1065, corroborating other evidence (human artefacts etc.). In contrast, the dating of two lava flows from the crater by the potassium-argon (K-Ar) method gave dates of 210,000 and 230,000 years old.[4] This discrepancy is now attributed to the presence of excess (non-radiogenic) argon already present in the lava flow at time zero. Geologists frequently use multiple methods on the same rock to establish the age, but there remains discussion in the published scientific literature about dating discrepancies. For example, Kröner *et al.* found that high-grade metamorphism of granitic and related rocks reduced their apparent U-Pb zircon ages from 1000 Ma down to 540 Ma, with results even from the

Sunset Crater Volcano, Arizona (Photo: ©)

same sample yielding U-Pb ages between 1072 Ma and 539 Ma.[5] In some cases, negative ages have been found.[6]

The third assumption, that rates of radioactive decay have remained constant for billions of years is also impossible to prove. It has been observed that under extreme conditions of high temperature, radiation or pressure, half-lives can be affected.[7] Further evidence for accelerated radioactive decay in the past is also found from radiohalos.[8] Radiohalos (or pleochroic halos) are microscopic, spherical shells of discolouration observed within minerals found within granites and other igneous rocks. Radiohalos of short-lived polonium found in Phanerozic granites were derived from uranium decay products which under measured decay rates today would have taken a long time to form.

Conclusions

It is now recognised that sedimentary rock layers once believed to have taken many years to form can be laid down very rapidly (i.e. in days or weeks) under catastrophic conditions (e.g. flood or tsunami). Radiometric dating methods are usually conducted on non-sedimentary rocks. Although the measurements both of half-lives and of the amount of isotopes present in a rock may be done to great accuracy, inferring the age of a rock sample from radiometric dating relies upon three crucial assumptions which cannot be verified in any particular case. Ages of lava flows determined by radiometric dating have been shown to be in error due to the presence of argon (not generated by radioactive decay) at time zero. Similarly, interaction of rock with its environment (non-closure) is known to produce erroneous ages. Accordingly, there are ongoing disputes in the scientific literature about the ages of particular rocks or formations. Discussion of discordant and discrepant results is a significant aspect of the geological literature.

Further Questions

1   Why are most sedimentary rocks not dateable using radiometric dating?

2   Why is carbon dating unsuitable for most specimens?

3   What can cause young volcanic rock to yield extremely old dates?

4   When the results from different dating methods are discordant, how can age be decided?

Case Study 3 Endnotes

1   Ager D (1981) *The Nature of the Stratigraphical Record* 54-106
2   A recent study documents many cases of ^{14}C detection in samples of coal, limestone and even diamonds previously thought to be too old to contain 14C. See Baumgardner JR *et al.* (2003) *The enigma of the ubiquity of ^{14}C in organic samples older than 100 ka Eos*, Transactions of the American Geophysical Union 84(46): F1570, Fall Meeting Supplement Abstract V32C-1045. http://www.agu.org/meetings/fm03/fm03-pdf/fm03-V32C.pdf or http://adsabs.harvard.edu/abs/2003AGUFM.V32C1045B You can view a copy of the poster here: http://www.icr.org/i/pdf/research/AGUC-14_Poster_Baumgardner.pdf
3   Weiner, J. S. (2004), *The Piltdown Forgery*, Oxford University Press, pp. 190–197, ISBN 0198607806
4   Dalrymple GB (1969) $^{40}Ar/^{36}Ar$ *Analyses of historical lava flows* Earth and Planetary Letters 6:47-55
5   Kröner A, Jaeckal P, Williams IS (1994) *Pb-Loss Patterns in Zircons from a High-Grade Metamorphic Terrain as Revealed by Different Dating Methods: U-Pb and Pb-Pb Ages for Igneous and Metamorphic Zircons from Northern Sri Lanka* Precambrian Research 66:151-81
6   Parrish RR (1990) *U-Pb Dating of Monazite and its Applications to Geological Problems* Canadian Journal of Earth Sciences 27:1431-50
7   Bosch F *et al.* (1996) *Observation of bound-state β– decay of fully ionized* ^{187}Re Physical Review Letters 77:5190–3
8   Snelling AA *et al.* (2003) *Abundant Po radiohalos in Phanerozic granites and timescale implications for their formation Eos*, Transactions of the American Geophysical Union 84(46): F1570, Fall Meeting Supplement, Abstract V32C-1046. http://www.agu.org/meetings/fm03/fm03-pdf/fm03-V32C.pdf or http://adsabs.harvard.edu/abs/2003AGUFM.V32C1046S You can view a copy of the poster here: http://www.icr.org/i/pdf/research/AGURadiohaloPoster_Snelling.pdf

Chapter 5
Diversity from Simplicity?

5.1 The Cambrian Explosion

About half of the major animal groups appear, fully formed, in the Cambrian strata of rocks, without any fossilised ancestors. This is shown in Figure 5.1.

This is how Richard Dawkins, the former Professor for the Public Understanding of Science at Oxford, describes it:

...the Cambrian strata of rocks, vintage about 600

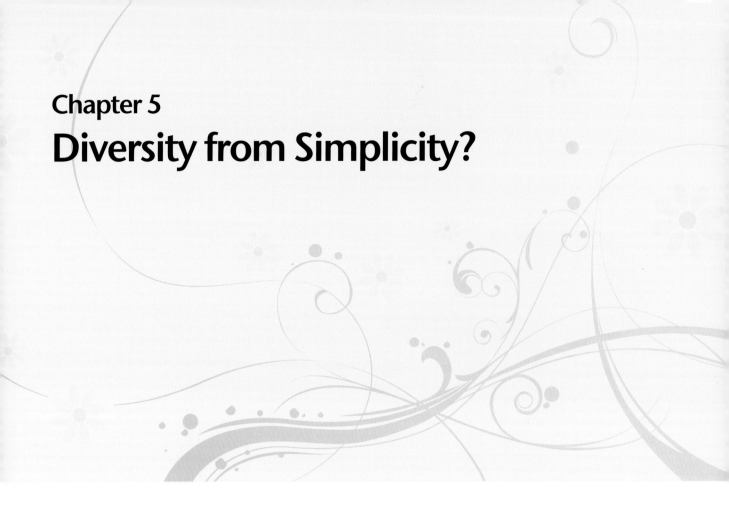

Figure 5.1 Sudden Emergence of Phyla in the Cambrian

million years, are the oldest ones in which we find most of the major invertebrate groups. And we find many of them already in an advanced state of evolution, the very first time they appear. It is as though they were just planted there, without any evolutionary history. Needless to say, this appearance of sudden planting has delighted creationists.[1]

How do Richard Dawkins and other evolutionists explain this abrupt appearance? For gradualistic evolution to be responsible, there must be a gap here – not just a small gap of one or two intermediate forms – but a truly massive gap of intermediates for at least 19 different phyla. Such a huge imperfection in the fossil record is the only explanation which evolutionists can give.

Why such a gap should occur is not clear. Sometimes it is claimed that the evolutionary ancestors of the Cambrian organisms were small and soft-bodied, and hence hard to fossilise. However, fossilised micro-organisms have been found in Pre-Cambrian rocks around the world, and many entirely soft-bodied animals have been found fossilised in Cambrian rocks. There does not seem to be a good reason why such a massive gap should exist. An example of an animal appearing abruptly without fossil ancestry in the Cambrian explosion is the velvet worm.

5.2 Velvet Worms

Figure 5.2 The Peripatus (Photo: iStock)

The velvet worms belong to the phylum Onychophora which means "claw-bearers". At least 80 living species are known, comprising two families: namely, the Peripatidae and the Peripatopsidae. They are found in tropical or sub-tropical regions of the Americas, Africa, South-eastern Asia and Australasia, which has the greatest variety. A living example of a velvet worm is the Peripatus (see Figure 5.2).

The Onychophora first appear in the fossil record in the Cambrian explosion. Although there have been more suggestions that the Onychophora are intermediate between annelids (segmented worms) and arthropods (a phylum including crustaceans and insects), according to Professor Donald Prothero:

> A classic example of a transitionary form links the arthropods to the lineage they split from in the Cambrian, namely, the nematode worms. These are the "velvet worms" or Onychophora. In many respects, the velvet worms resemble nematodes, but they also have key attributes of the arthropods - most notably segmented legs that end in hooked claws. They also have many other features found in arthropods but not nematodes, including an outer layer made of chitin, which they moult on a regular basis, antennae, compound eyes and arthropod-like mouthparts.[2]

Unlike other scientists, Professor Prothero suggests that the velvet worms are derived from nematodes (roundworms), which are one of the most common phyla of animals, with more than 20,000 living species. Fossil nematodes are relatively rare, but they do exist. The best examples of ancient nematodes have been found preserved in amber and dated from the Cenozoic period. Another example is a putative nematode (*Captivonema cretacea*) from the early Cretaceous. Whether nematode fossils will ever be found in Cambrian (or Pre-Cambrian) strata remains to be seen, and according to Professor Simon Conway Morris (University of Cambridge):

> To date, however, the fossil record throws no useful light on the origin of the nematodes.[3]

One of the reasons suggested for the absence of nematode fossils in Cambrian strata is their microscopic size and possession of soft body parts. Nevertheless, current research suggests that at least part of the Cambrian strata was laid down very rapidly.[4] This explains the amazing fossil preservation of myriads of soft-bodied creatures – but it gives no support for the idea that velvet worms are transitional between nematodes and arthropods. Soft tissue fossils have also been found in the Cambrian strata from Chengjiang, near the city of Kunming in Yunnan Province, China. Apart from a vast array of arthropods, representatives of Lobopoda - segmented animals resembling (and maybe including) Onychophora - have been found in these mudstone sediments. In addition, several examples of Nematomorpha have been discovered. These creatures are similar to nematodes but are a distinct phylum, with many modern representatives, such as the horsehair worms.

So Professor Prothero's suggestion that the Onychophora are transitional between nematodes and arthropods is not borne out by the actual evidence presented in the fossil record. It is based on the rather superficial assessment that "velvet worms resemble nematodes". He concludes this section of his article by stating:

> You could not ask for a better "missing link" between the nematodes and the arthropods, except it's not missing - we've known about velvet worms for over a century in both the living fauna and the fossil record.[5]

Although this statement is somewhat misleading, at least Professor Prothero highlights the fact that Onychophora themselves are extant today – they might be considered "living fossils". The ancient Cambrian species *Aysheaia* seems remarkably similar to the modern *Peripatus* shown in Figure 5.2.

5.3 Ancient Chordates and the Emergence of Fish

It has also been suggested that:

> Another key transition in animal evolution was the appearance of the vertebrates. For more than a century, evidence has been accumulating from anatomy and embryology that the Chordata phylum (which includes the vertebrates) evolved from the echinoderms - sea urchins, starfish and their kin. This has now been corroborated by molecular biology. We also have an array of fossils and living organisms to tell the story of the transition.[4]

The dogmatic assertion that chordates (and therefore vertebrates) have evolved from echinoderm ("spiny-skin") ancestors are not backed up by the evidence. Although fossils of sea urchins and starfish (and their kin) do not appear in Cambrian strata, there are some strange and extinct echinoderms. These include edrioasteroids, eocrinoids and helicoplacoids.

In 2004, Shu and his team described another group of early Cambrian echinoderms, the vetulocystids.[6] In the same issue of the journal *Nature*, Andrew Smith, Merit Researcher at the Natural History Museum in London, wrote a review of the Shu paper entitled *Echinoderm Roots*.[7]

Figure 5.3 is faithfully redrawn from Smith's paper and illustrates the main deuterostome groups. Deuterostomes comprise a superphylum which encompasses the echinoderms and the chordates (including the vertebrates). You will notice that this diagram provides no support for the suggestion that the Chordata phylum (and hence the vertebrates) evolved from the echinoderms.

Furthermore, Andrew Smith states in this *Nature* article:

> There is now direct fossil evidence that all of the major deuterostome groups were established by about 520 million years ago. Fossil vertebrates (yunnanozoans), tunicates and both asymmetric and radiate echinoderms (homalozoans, helicoplacoids) have all now been discovered in early Cambrian deposits.

Nevertheless, Prothero's article in *New Scientist* insists that chordates have evolved from echinoderms. Although there is no evidence for this in the fossil record, it suggests possible intermediate forms. These include hemichordates (e.g. acorn worms and filter feeding pterobranchs) and more particularly tunicates. He states categorically:

> Next up are the sea squirts, or tunicates. Though adult sea squirts are similar to pterobranchs, the larvae look much like primitive fish, with a muscular tail supported by a "backbone" of cartilage, the notochord - the defining feature of the chordates.[4]

Although this is somewhat confusing, it

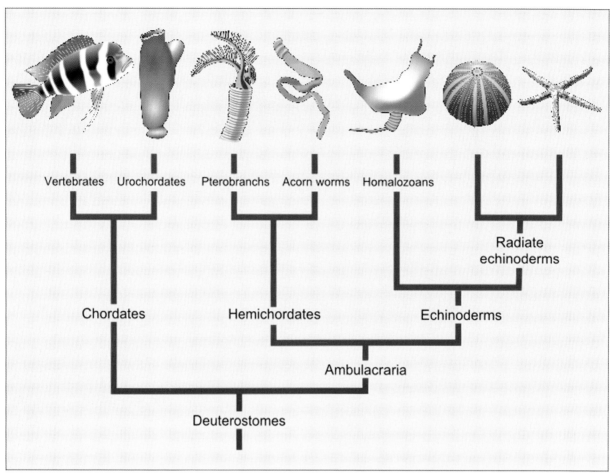

Figure 5.3 Deuterostome Groups

states correctly that sea squirts are classified as chordates since their larvae possess a notochord (cartilaginous rod). This is shown in Figure 5.4.

Chen reported the discovery of eight specimens of an early Cambrian fossil tunicate *Shankouclava* near Kunming (South China).[8] Again the fossil record clearly indicates that there were tunicates in the early Cambrian. Accordingly, it is not possible to conclude on the basis of the actual evidence that tunicates have evolved from echinoderms or from anything else. It is simply inferred from the general appearance of extant[9] forms of these phyla. Maybe this is an alternative updated example of "phylogeny recapitulates ontogeny" that was originally proposed by Ernst Haeckel on the basis of his dubious embryonic diagrams.

Nevertheless, appearances can be very deceptive, as Figure 5.4 clearly indicates. It is worth considering whether the suggestion

that sea squirt larvae "look like primitive fish" has any basis in reality. Nevertheless, the good professor does not give up:

> The transitional sequence continues with a group of obscure invertebrates called the lancelets. These *resemble* [emphasis added] tunicate larvae, and probably evolved from a tunicate-like creature through "neoteny" - retention of juvenile features in adulthood. With a notochord, muscular tail, gill slits, a digestive tract along the belly and many other chordate features, lancelets are the most fish-like invertebrates known. They have been around since the Cambrian: we have a number of good lancelet fossils such as Pikaia from the Burgess Shale and similar fossils from Chengjiang.[7]

What is certain is that these fossil lancelets appear very similar to the modern and not so obscure *Amphioxus* (a living example of a cephalochordate), which is alive

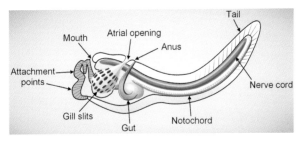

Figure 5.4 Tunicate Larva

Figure 5.5 Amphioxus

and well on planet Earth. *Amphioxus* (see Figure 5.5) is extremely common in shallow sandy environments such as Discovery Bay in Jamaica, where up to 5,000 living individuals per square metre of sand have been reported. *Amphioxus* is commercially harvested and eaten by humans and domestic animals in some parts of Asia.

Of particular interest are the ancient fish fossils that have been found in the Cambrian. For example, in 1999, Shu and his group reported finding two species of ancient jawless fish, namely, *Haikouichthys ercaicunensis* and *Myllokunmingia fengjiaoa*. A report of this discovery is found on the BBC website.[10] In this article, Conway Morris is quoted:

> Until now, the early history of the fish has been extremely sporadic and sometimes difficult to interpret. This discovery shows that fish evolved much earlier than was thought. It indicates also that the rates of evolution in the oceans during the Cambrian period must have been exceptionally fast. Not only do we see the appearance of the fish, but also a whole range of different animal types.

Also in 1999, Chen *et al.* reported the finding of another early Cambrian chordate which they called *Haikouella lancelet*.[11] In their paper, they state that *Haikouella* has evidence of:

> ...a heart, ventral and dorsal aorta, an anterior branchial arterial, gill filaments, a caudal

Haikouella (Photo: ©)

projection, a neural cord with a relatively large brain, a head with possible lateral eyes, and a ventrally situated buccal cavity with short tentacles. These findings indicate that *Haikouella* probably represents a very early craniate-like chordate that lived near the beginning of the Cambrian period during the main burst of the Cambrian explosion.

More recently, Shu reported further studies made possible by the discovery of numerous specimens of the early Cambrian vertebrate *Haikouichthys ercaicunensis*.[12] The paper presents further evidence that Haikouichthys was a fossil agnathan. Agnathans are jawless fish and are represented today by hagfish and lampreys. Professor Prothero admits to the presence of these ancient vertebrates in the Cambrian:

> Cambrian rocks in China have also yielded fossils of the earliest-known vertebrates, the soft-bodied jawless fish *Haikouella, Haikouichthys,* and *Myllokunmingia*. These creatures did not yet have a hard bony skeleton, but have all the other features of jawless fish supported by a skeleton of cartilage.

But then he says something quite remarkable and illuminating:

> Placed in sequence, the acorn worms, tunicates, lancelets and soft-bodied jawless fish show the complete set of steps needed to evolve a vertebrate from an invertebrate ancestor.

This is merely armchair biology. As we have seen, the sequence is chosen on the assumption of stepwise evolution from an invertebrate to a vertebrate, and it is then presented to show the steps that are needed. Furthermore, the suggestion by Prothero that molecular biology corroborates this interpretation is similarly without support in the academic literature. *Zhong et al.* recently (2009) published a paper entitled *Revaluation of deuterostome phylogeny and evolutionary relationships among chordate subphyla using mitogenome data.*[13] The authors state in their abstract (emphasis added):

> *The traditional knowledge in textbooks* indicated that cephalochordates were the closest relatives to vertebrates among all extant organisms. However, *this opinion was challenged* by several recent phylogenetic studies using hundreds of nuclear genes. The researchers suggested that urochordates, but not cephalochordates, should be the closest living relatives to vertebrates. In the present study, by using data generated from hundreds of mtDNA sequences, we revalue the deuterostome phylogeny in terms of whole mitochondrial genomes (mitogenomes). *Our results firmly demonstrate that each of extant deuterostome phyla and chordate subphyla is monophyletic.* But the results present several alternative phylogenetic trees depending on different sequence datasets used in the analysis. Although no clear phylogenetic relationships are obtained, those trees indicate that the ancient common ancestor diversified rapidly soon after their appearance in the early Cambrian and generated all major deuterostome lineages during a short historical period, which is consistent with "Cambrian explosion" revealed by paleontologists.

5.4 From Water to Land

One of the major predictions of neo-Darwinian theory is the existence of "transitional forms". These are organisms that must have developed, according to the evolutionary model, as one major group evolved into another. Transitional forms would stand morphologically (i.e. in body form) between the ancestral and descendant groups. Their fossils would also be expected to lie between at least some of those of their ancestors and of all those of their descendants in the vertical sequence of rock layers. Since every group of organisms is thought to have evolved from an earlier group, transitional forms between groups ought to be common. However, convincing examples of such transitional forms are rare; there are far fewer than evolutionary theory would predict. This seems especially true of the most easily preserved groups in the fossil record – shallow marine invertebrates such as molluscs and brachiopods. From an evolutionary perspective this is counter-intuitive because these are precisely the groups that would be expected to yield the most convincing series of transitional forms.

Nevertheless, there are some fossil

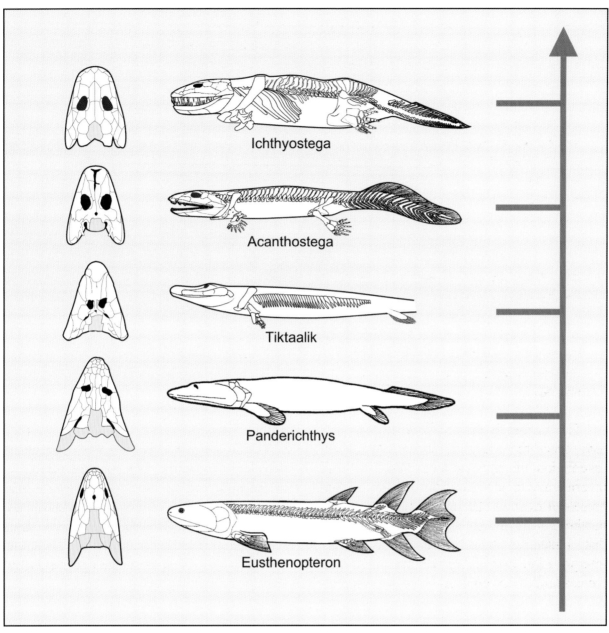

Figure 5.6 Proposed Transition from Fish to Tetrapod

organisms, mostly among the vertebrates, which are claimed to be transitional forms. Among them are the fossils found in Upper Devonian sediments (conventionally dated to around 359-385 million years ago) which are said to document the evolution of the first tetrapods (i.e. vertebrates with four limbs) from fish-like ancestors. The Devonian tetrapods, represented by creatures such as *Acanthostega* and *Ichthyostega*, are one-metre-long aquatic animals thought to have lived a predatory lifestyle in weed-infested shallow water.

Evolutionists have sought the ancestry of these among the lobe-finned fishes which form a major part of the fish faunas of Devonian sediments. One of these, a fish called *Elpistostege*, is thought to have been very tetrapod-like in overall body shape, although its remains are very incomplete and its anatomy is poorly known. Complete specimens of a similar lobe-fin, called *Panderichthys*, however, confirm the tetrapod-like impression. *Panderichthys* had a superficially crocodile-like skull with dorsally-placed eyes, a straight tail, and a slightly flattened body without dorsal or anal fins. Furthermore, like tetrapods, but

Tiktaalik (Photo: mmechtley/Flickr)

unlike all other fishes, both *Elpistostege* and *Panderichthys* had frontal bones in the skull roof. This is illustrated in Figure 5.6.

In 2006, the evolutionary transition between fish and tetrapods again came to prominence when a new fossil lobe-fin called *Tiktaalik* was described in the journal *Nature*.[14] The name *Tiktaalik* means "large freshwater fish" in the traditional language of the Nunavut region of Arctic Canada where its remains were found. Several specimens, some extremely well preserved in three dimensions and with parts of the skeleton still articulated, were discovered in a 15-cm siltstone layer in the middle part of a rock unit called the Fram Formation.

Tiktaalik has been given the conventional geological age of 375 million years. The choice of this date is for two reasons. First, this is the age ascribed to the siltstone sediments. Secondly, the precise age was chosen as it fits the hypothesis that *Tiktallik* is a transitional form between the "earlier" fish (e.g. *Panderichthys,* conventionally dated at 380 million years) and the "later" tetrapods (e.g. *Acanthostega,* dated between 360 to 370

million years).

Upon reconstruction, the specimens revealed a creature that was, in effect, "a better-preserved version of *Elpistostege*".[15] Like its previously-discovered counterparts, *Tiktaalik* had a flattened body, gills, bony scales, and fins with fin rays. However, *Tiktaalik* had a longer snout, larger ribs and a wider spiracle (small gill slit), and lacked a bony gill cover. *Tiktaalik* also displayed some features of the neck and the fin skeleton that suggested that its body could be supported in shallow water or on land. In other words, *Tiktaalik* seemed to be even more tetrapod-like than *Panderichthys* or *Elpistostege*. Neil Shubin, a member of the team that discovered *Tiktaalik*, commented: "We describe this as a 'fishopod': part fish, part tetrapod".[16]

What is more, *Tiktaalik* was found in sediments that are dated as older than those containing *Acanthostega* and *Ichthyostega*, but younger than those containing *Panderichthys*; it apparently lies between its presumed ancestors and descendants in the geological sequence. It is not hard to see why this discovery was regarded as important confirmatory evidence of the hypothesised evolutionary transition between the lobe-finned fishes and their tetrapod descendants.

How, then, do sceptics of neo-Darwinism evaluate the status of *Tiktaalik*? While this creature does seem to be a morphological and stratigraphic intermediate, comprising a strange mixture of fish-like features and tetrapod-like features, it should be noted that many organisms, both fossil and living, exhibit a similar mosaic distribution of character traits. A living example is the platypus, which has features of both mammals (hair, milk production) and reptiles (egg-laying). The late Stephen Jay Gould called such organisms "mosaic forms" or "chimeras".[17] When these mosaic forms occur in the right part of the geological record, they are readily interpreted as evolutionary intermediates linking major groups.

However, the mosaic pattern also poses a problem for evolutionary scenarios, because it often makes it difficult to identify organisms or groups of organisms that possess the 'right' combination of characters to be considered part of an evolutionary lineage. Consider the tetrapod-like lobe-fins *Panderichthys* and *Elpistostege*. Despite their appearance, these fish have some unique characters (such as the design of the vertebrae) that rule them out as tetrapod ancestors. At best, evolutionists can only claim that they are a model of the kind of fish that must have served as that ancestor. The same problem is encountered with the Devonian tetrapods. For example, *Ichthyostega* is described as "a very strange animal, and parts of it are like no other known tetrapod or fish".[18] Similarly, the shoulder girdles of the Devonian tetrapods "are not obviously halfway in structure between those of fishes and those of later tetrapods but have some unique and some unexpected features". Another example is *Livoniana*, a so-called 'near tetrapod' known from two lower jaw fragments. It possesses a curious mixture of fish-like and tetrapod-like characteristics, but it also has up to five rows of teeth, a feature not seen either in the fishes from which it is

thought to be descended nor the tetrapods into which it is said to be evolving.[19] A similar observation can be made with *Tiktaalik*, which has an unossified backbone with an unusually large number of vertebrae – more than in its presumed ancestors or descendants.

It is also worth noting that one of the key morphological transitions between fish and tetrapods – the purported change from paired fins to limbs with digits – remains undocumented by fossils. One of the most striking features of *Tiktaalik* is the structural arrangement of its pectoral fin, in which the individual bony elements are so well preserved that detailed studies were able to elucidate how it might have moved during life.[20] It appears that *Tiktaalik* had a sturdy, though highly flexible, fin with "wrist-like" and "elbow-like" joints that would have allowed the animal to prop itself up on a substrate. Nevertheless, *Tiktaalik* is still clearly a fish with fins and fin rays – it does not possess the fingers and toes that mark out the tetrapods. As Ahlberg and Clack write in their commentary in *Nature*:

> Although these small distal bones bear some resemblance to tetrapod digits in terms of their function and range of movement, they are still very much components of a fin. There remains a large morphological gap between them and digits as seen in, for example, Acanthostega: if the digits evolved from these distal bones, the process must have involved considerable developmental repatterning.[15]

Fossil trackways near Wystȩpa, Poland
(Photo: mmechtley/Flickr)

From a design perspective, *Tiktaalik* appears beautifully constructed for its life in an aquatic habitat where the water was not deep enough to support the body. Many of the "fish-like tetrapods" and "tetrapod-like fish" found in Devonian sediments, *Tiktaalik* included, are thought to have been ambush predators lurking among the tangled weeds and roots of shallow pools and other similar environments. They were therefore equipped with characteristics appropriate to that habitat (e.g. crocodile-like morphology with dorsally placed eyes, limbs and tails made for swimming, internal gills) that gave them the ability to function both in the water and, to some extent, on land. In this context, their morphologically intermediate characters can be understood as a highly efficient design for life in the marginal aquatic ecosystems in which they lived.

5.5 Polish Trackways

All of these arguments, however, have been somewhat overshadowed by the discovery of fossil trackways of tetrapods that have been found in Poland. The remarkable, but also somewhat inconvenient, aspect from an evolutionary perspective is their age. The trackways have been given a conventional geological age of approximately 395 million years old.[21] In the words of PZ Myers:

> Just to put that in perspective, Tiktaalik, probably the most famous specimen illustrating an early stage of the transition to land, is younger at 375 million years, but is more primitive in having less developed, more fin-like limbs. So what we've got is a set of footprints that tell us the actual age of the transition by vertebrates from water to land had to be much, much earlier than was expected, by tens of millions of years.[22]

The trackways are clearly made by terrestrial tetrapods. The distinct footprints from both the front and hind limbs also demonstrate that the creatures had had jointed limbs that lifted and propelled them forward in the mud. The creatures are considerably larger than either of the famous Devonian tetrapods Ichthyostega and Acanthostega. Again in the words of PZ Myers:

> What's it all mean? Well, there's the obvious implication that if you want to find earlier examples of the tetrapod transition, you should look in rocks that are about 400 million years old or older. However, it's a little more complicated than that, because the mix of existing fossils tells us that there were viable, long-lasting niches for a diversity of fish, fishapods, and tetrapods that temporally coexisted for a long period of time... Paleontologists are simply sampling bits and pieces of the model line-up and trying to sort out the relationships and timing of their origin. The other phenomenon here is a demonstration of the spottiness of the fossil record... That complicates the story, too; not only do we have diverse stages of the tetrapod transition happily living together in time, but there may be a bit of selective fossilization going on, that only preserves some of the more derived forms living in taphonomically[23] favorable environments.

5.6 Summary

Although *Tiktaalik* is a lobe-finned fish with an unusual combination of characters shared with other lobe-fins and aquatic tetrapods of the Upper Devonian, its privileged place as a transitional creature between earlier fish and later Devonian amphibians has been threatened by the discovery of Polish trackways made by terrestrial creatures that have been conventionally dated as considerably older.

5.7 Further Questions

1   Why is the Cambrian Explosion problematic to the concept of the gradual emergence of complex organisms?

2   What conditions are required to preserve soft-bodied creatures such as the velvet worm and nematodes?

3   Is it plausible to say that soft-bodied animals are rarely preserved and that this explains their absence in the Pre-Cambrian?

4   What, if anything, does Professor Prothero's "complete set of steps needed to evolve a vertebrate from an invertebrate ancestor" tell us about the real biological world?

5   What does it take to develop a heart and circulatory system that are found in jawless fish (ancient and modern)?

Chapter 5 Endnotes

1   Dawkins R (1986) *The Blind Watchmaker* page 229

2   New Scientist 1st March 2008 Page 36

3   Conway Morris S (2004) *Darwin's Dilemma: The realities of the Cambrian Explosion* Philosophical Transactions of the Royal Society 361:1069–83

4   New Scientist 1st March 2008 Page 36

5   Gabbott SE *et al.* (2008) Journal of the Geological Society 165:307-18

6   Shu DG *et al. Ancestral echinoderms from the Chengjiang deposits of China.* Nature 430, 422-8

7   http://www.nhm.ac.uk/research-curation/staff-directory/palaeontology/smith/assets/pdf10.pdf

8   http://www.pnas.org/content/100/14/8314.full (freely available)

9   living

10   http://news.bbc.co.uk/1/hi/sci/tech/504776.stm

11   Chen J-Y, Huang D-Y, Li C-W (1999) *An early Cambrian craniate-like chordate* Nature 402: 518-22

12   Shu DG *et al.* (2003) *Head and backbone of the Early Cambrian vertebrate Haikouichthys* Nature 421:526-9

13   *Revaluation of deuterostome phylogeny and evolutionary relationships among chordate subphyla using mitogenome data* J Genet Genomics (2009) 36:151-60

14   Daeschler EB, Shubin NH, Jenkins FA (2006) *A Devonian tetrapod-like fish and the evolution of the tetrapod body plan* Nature 440:757-63

15   Ahlberg PE, Clack JA (2006) *A firm step from water to land* Nature 440:747-9

16   Holmes B (2006) *The fish that headed for land* New Scientist 2546 page 14

17   Wise KP (1994) *The origin of life's major groups* pp.211-234 in: Moreland JP (editor), The Creation Hypothesis: Scientific Evidence for an Intelligent Designer, InterVarsity Press, Downers Grove

18   Clack JA (2002) *Gaining Ground: The Origin and Evolution of Tetrapods* Indiana University Press, Bloomington

19   Ahlberg PE, Luksevics E, Mark-Kurik E (2000) A *near-tetrapod from the Baltic Middle Devonian* Palaeontology 43: 533-48

20   Shubin NH, Daeschler EB, Jenkins FA (2006) *The pectoral fin of Tiktaalik roseae and the origin of the tetrapod limb* Nature 440:764-71

21   Niedzwiedzki G, Szrek P, Narkiewicz K, Narkiewicz M, Ahlberg PE (2010) Tetrapod trackways from the early Middle Devonian period of Poland. Nature 463:43-8

22   http://scienceblogs.com/pharyngula/2006/04/tiktaalik_makes_another_gap.php

23   Taphonomy - the study of the conditions and processes by which organisms become fossilised.

CASE STUDY 4
Trilobite Eyes: Out of the blue?

According to consensus among evolutionists, trilobites are some of the oldest organisms known from the fossilised past. They were evidently sea creatures that walked on the sea floor (Figure CS4.1). Although trilobites have three body sections: cephalon, thorax and pygidium, they are called trilobites because they have three longitudinal lobes (Figure CS4.2) – these are the central axial lobe, and two symmetrical pleural lobes that flank the axis.

There are a very large variety of trilobites and they are found in Cambrian through Devonian and Carboniferous up to Permian strata. Thus, traditional dating for trilobite fossils, which are very numerous among animal fossils, would be 550 million years ago through to 250 million years ago. A remarkable fact is that precursors to these creatures have never been found. Arthropods (many-legged creatures) appear abruptly in the Cambrian strata, and do not show evidence of

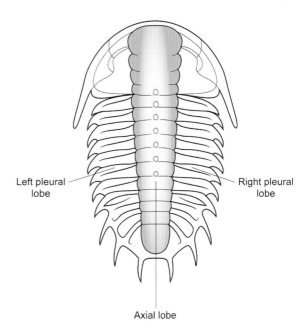

Figure CS4.2 The three longitudinal lobes of the trilobite.

Left pleural lobe

Right pleural lobe

Axial lobe

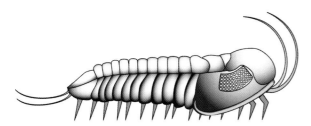

Figure CS4.1 An impression of how a living trilobite would have looked on the sea floor.

development – rather there is a large variety of trilobite fossils in these layers, which strongly suggests that all these varieties always existed alongside each other.

Trilobite Eyes

Figure CS4.3 The double image occurring in a natural crystal of calcite (calcium carbonate, $CaCO_3$)

What is particularly fascinating is that the compound eyes of trilobites are not made of protein but of calcite, which is a mineral. But the problem with natural crystals of calcite ($CaCO_3$) is that they give double images, as illustrated in Figure CS4.3. The reason for this phenomenon is that some transparent materials are birefringent: this means they have two refractive indices. To understand birefringent materials it is important to know about polarisation of light: the fact that light can have a plane of "orientation" as well as a direction. When a nonpolarised beam of light enters a birefringent crystal, it splits into two beams that travel at different speeds, and therefore take different directions. One of these beams is called the "extraordinary ray" and is polarised in a plane that includes the crystal's optical axis (this is a direction vector such that light parallel to that direction suffers no birefringence). The other beam is polarised perpendicular to the optical axis and is called the "ordinary ray". Since the two component light beams travel independently in separate directions and at different velocities, objects viewed through the crystal have a double image. This happens for all lines of sight except when viewing directly along the optical axis.

Calcite is a birefringent mineral with just one optical axis, but there are other transparent materials which have more than one optical axis. Through a polarised filter the double image in calcite can be removed, by rotating the filter such that the blocking plane of the filter includes the optical axis.

So were trilobites seeing double? Here are some remarkable facts about the vision of trilobite eyes. First, the individual lenses of the trilobite eye are oriented such that the line of sight is directly along the optical axis, so that double images were not observed by the humble creature. Secondly, the depth of field is very large. Objects remain in focus at a distance of a few millimetres up to infinity.

And thirdly, sophisticated control of spherical aberration (image distortion) is in evidence. By shaping the lens in such a way that there is a point of inflexion on a radial outward from the centre, it was discovered by Descartes and Huygens (as illustrated in Figures CS4.4 and CS4.5) that there are certain optimal shapes that remove spherical aberration from images and keep the image in sharp focus. What is quite astonishing is that the shape of the trilobite lenses is in accordance with the shapes[1] discovered in the 17th Century, by Descartes (1596-1650) and Huygens (1629-1695). The lenses of calcite in trilobite eyes have these very shapes. A fourth remarkable fact is that one group of trilobites (the phacopid trilobites) have eyes with fewer and larger lenses separated from each other (called schizochroal lenses) and in these cases an intralensar material is also attached to the main lens, which further sharpens the image.[2] The upper part of this doublet lens is particularly important for seeing in water, since the additional material has a different refractive index and enables the sharp focus to be maintained over a long depth of field.

In his book of 1993, Levi-Setti states:

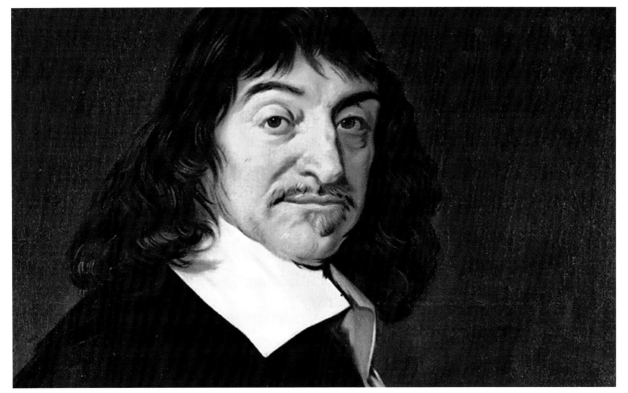

Rene Descartes who (with Huygens) discovered the shape necessary to minimize spherical aberration in lenses. (Photo: ©)

Trilobites had solved a very elegant physical problem and apparently knew about Fermat's principle, Abbe's sine law, Snell's laws of refraction and the optics of birefringent crystals… Putting such statements in an anthropomorphic style does not remove the severe challenge to the idea that simple mutation and natural selection could evolve such physical optimisation.[3]

The eyes of trilobites vary from closely packed, very small lenses – called holochroal designs – to fewer larger lenses (schizochroal and abathocroal designs). The sophistication of the optics, using lenses made from birefringent material such that the optical axis of each of the calcite components in the lens is aligned with the line of sight, is astonishing.[4] That, furthermore, each of the hundreds (and in the holochroal cases, thousands) of lens shapes is correctly shaped (identical to the Descartes and Huygens optics) as well as uniquely aligned is remarkable. These facts, coupled with the lack of any precursors to trilobites in the Pre-Cambrian strata, challenge the view that these creatures came from simpler ancestors. An alternative view is that they are part of a family of animals designed for a sea floor environment.

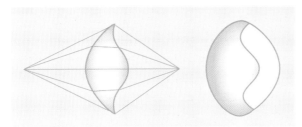

Figure CS4.4 The Descartes lens designed for minimal aberration (left) is found in the lens of the trilobite Crozonaspis (right).

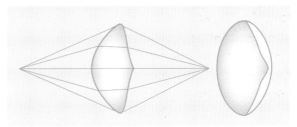

Figure CS4.5 Huygens' lens design for minimal aberration (left) is found in the lens of the trilobite Dalmanitina (right)

Further Questions

1   What do all lenses suffer from at the edges?

2   How do trilobite lenses minimise the edge difficulty?

3   What is the material that the lenses in the eyes of trilobites are made from?

4   Birefringence causes double images to occur – how do the lenses of trilobites avoid this?

Case Study 4 Endnotes

1   Clarkson ENK, Levi-Setti R (1975) *Trilobite eyes and the optics of Descartes and Huygens* Nature 254:663-7
2   See website by SM Gon III http://www.trilobites.info/eyes.htm In this website, there is a wealth of information as to the different types of trilobites and in particular a very useful description of the calcite compound eye structure. Gon has a disclaimer against intelligent design, and argues that the eyes are an example of evolution. The fact that there are no precursors in the Precambrian strata strongly suggests that the trilobite family represents an example of a creature designed for its environment. The sophisticated optics of the trilobite eye is entirely consistent with this position. The reader is encouraged to examine the evidence and draw his own conclusions.
3   Levi-Setti R (1993) *Trilobites: A photographic atlas, Second edition* The University of Chicago Press, Chicago p.33
4   Clarkson E, Levi-Setti R, Horvath G (2006) *The eyes of trilobites: The oldest preserved visual system* Arthropod Structure and Development 35:247-59

Chapter 6
From Dinosaurs to Birds?

For all their enduring appeal, there is much confusion about what a dinosaur actually is. Some people mistakenly assume that any large, extinct animal is a dinosaur. In fact, dinosaurs are only one of many groups that have no living descendants. Dinosaurs were reptiles, but they were unlike any reptiles living today. Living reptiles, such as crocodiles, tortoises and lizards, are sprawlers. Their legs extend sideways and bend at the knees and elbows.

Dinosaurs, however, stood fully upright with their legs tucked beneath their bodies. The upright posture of dinosaurs meant they had distinctive vertebrae, hips, knees, ankles and feet. These are some of the characteristics that scientists use to define the dinosaur group. All known dinosaurs lived on the land; marine reptiles (e.g. plesiosaurs) and flying reptiles (e.g. pterosaurs) were not part of the dinosaur group.

6.1 Fossil Evidence of Dinosaurs

The fossil remains of dinosaurs have been found on every continent, including Antarctica. Most consist of bones and teeth because these are resistant to decay, but sometimes soft parts are discovered. There are rare occasions when the imprint of a dinosaur's skin has been found. Many trackways of footprints, like those in Rioja, Spain, have been discovered.

Even dinosaur eggs, embryos and hatchlings are preserved in some locations. Evidence of diet comes from the examination of stomach contents and even fossilised dinosaur dung! As a result, we have a wealth of information about dinosaurs, although, of course, there is still much that we do not know.

6.2 The Major Groups of Dinosaurs

Figure 6.1 The skeleton of the theropod Tyrannosaurus Rex (Photo: iStock)

The dinosaurs fall into two groups, based on differences in the structure of the pelvis: those with "reptile-like" hips and those with "bird-like" hips. The "reptile hips" include the theropods (the flesh-eating dinosaurs) and the sauropodomorphs (the large long-necked plant-eaters). The "bird hips" include the ornithopods (two-legged plant-eaters), the pachycephalosaurs (the bone-headed dinosaurs), the ceratopsians (the horn-faced dinosaurs), the stegosaurs (with plates and spines) and the ankylosaurs (the armoured dinosaurs). Let us briefly consider each of these groups.

Theropods

Most members of this group had teeth serrated like steak knives, and sharply curved hand claws. The group includes some of the largest land predators that ever existed, such as *Tyrannosaurus Rex* (Figure 6.1) and *Giganotosaurus*, which were twelve metres or more in length. Other theropods, however, were small and slender. *Compsognathus*, from southern Germany, was only 60 centimetres long and most of that was its tail.

Sauropodomorphs

This group includes the gigantic sauropods and the smaller prosauropods. The prosauropods (e.g. *Plateosaurus*) stood on two legs and had grasping hands. By contrast, the sauropods were four-footed giants with extremely long necks and tails. They include the largest land animals of all time: *Argentinosaurus* may have weighed about 70 tonnes.

Ornithopods

This group of two-legged plant-eaters includes small (2-3 metres) and large (15-20 metres) varieties. One group of ornithopods, the hadrosaurs ("duck-billed" dinosaurs), possessed remarkable head crests. The most popular explanation for these crests is that they were visual signals. However, their hollow shape and connection to the nasal passages suggests they may also have acted as resonating chambers to produce sounds.

Pachycephalosaurs

These strange dinosaurs look similar to the ornithopods but had enormously thickened skull roofs. The name of this group means "bone-headed". They probably engaged in "head-butting" behaviour like that seen in some modern animals, perhaps to establish the "pecking order" in the social group. Not all experts are convinced about this, but it seems difficult to explain the thick skulls otherwise.

Ceratopsians

Although the name means 'horn face', not all the ceratopsians possessed horns. The group includes the ceratopsids (e.g. *Triceratops*) which had horns over the nose and eyes and long bony frills at the back of the skull. Then there are the protoceratopsids, smaller and less adorned but still possessing a bony frill.

Finally there is *Psittacosaurus*, an unusual ceratopsian (see Figure 6.2) which has neither horns nor a frill. However, like other members of the group, it has a "parrot-like" beak tipped with an extra bone (called the rostral).

Stegosaurs

The name of this group, meaning "roofed lizard", refers to the rows of flat plates or spines that all stegosaurs had along their backs. They had additional spines on their shoulders and on their tails. The most well-known member of the group, *Stegosaurus*, had large diamond-shaped plates on its back. They may have acted as heat exchangers to regulate body temperature.

Ankylosaurs

These were four-legged dinosaurs with armour made up of bony plates embedded in the skin. In some types, such as *Euoplocephalus,* the rows of plates were fused into a single solid piece of armour. Some had long spines along their sides and some had bony tail clubs. Ankylosaurs even had armour-plated skulls with bony eyelid covers. They were the "armoured vehicles" of the dinosaur world.

Many people mistakenly believe that modern-day animals are "more advanced" than those that have become extinct. However, it is difficult to regard animals like dinosaurs as "primitive". Think, for instance, about the giant sauropods. They were constructed like

Figure 6.2 The skeleton of Psittacosaurus – an example of a ceratopsian (Photo: iStock)

suspension bridges, with the front and back legs as the upright towers of the bridge and the backbone as the road running between them. The long neck was counterbalanced by the long tail and along the backbone ran a massive, slightly elastic tendon. As Dr David Norman of the Sedgwick Museum in Cambridge has written:

> This arrangement allowed these dinosaurs to have an economical system for supporting both neck and tail, which did not require vast amounts of muscular power. In life these animals would almost certainly have been able to stand at rest with both neck and tail suspended clear of the ground with very little effort.[1]

In the biomechanics of these dinosaurs we see the application of sound engineering principles. Was the neo-Darwinian mechanism (natural selection acting upon random mutations) really responsible for such remarkable adaptations?

6.3 The Origin of Birds

The modern form of the theory that birds are related to theropod dinosaurs dates from the 1970s when J. H. Ostrom described similarities between *Archaeopteryx,* a Jurassic bird or feathered reptile (see below), and *Deinonychus*, a theropod.[2] *Deinonychus* (discovered in 1969) was 2.5 to 4 metres long and is thought to be 110 million years old. It has long been believed that it and similar "raptors" were feathered.

The Chinese Fossils

Fossils from Cretaceous sediments in China are now claimed to confirm this theory. These sediments are interpreted as remains of ancient lakes which once covered the Liaoning Province in north-eastern China, during the Cretaceous period. These layers contain many fossils of plants, insects, molluscs, crustaceans, fish, frogs, salamanders, turtles, lizards,

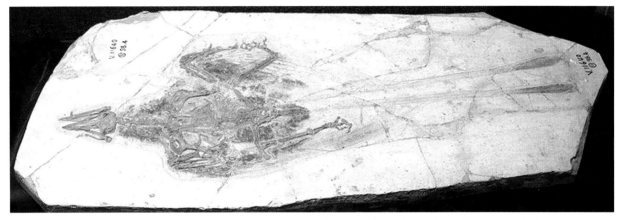

Figure 6.3 A specimen of Confuciusornis sanctus, on display at the Paleozoological Museum of China. (Photo: Wikimedia Commons)

mammals and birds, such as *Confuciusornis sanctus* (see Figure 6.3), together with well preserved theropod dinosaurs such as *Sinosauropteryx prima*.

Their importance lies in the fact that some have remains of filaments that are thought to

Figure 6.4 Fossil replica GMV 2124 of Sinosauropteryx (Compsognathidae), from the early Cretaceaous Yixian formation in the Liaoning Province of China; now in the Staatliches Museum für Naturkunde Karlsruhe, Germany. (Photo: Wikimedia Commons)

be precursors to feathers (proto-feathers) and others had feathers.

One of the first fossils from this region was **Confuciusornis**[3]. This is evidently a bird from Jurassic sediments. However, the real excitement was caused by the discovery of small theropod dinosaurs which appeared to have remains of filament-like structures which some consider to be proto-feathers (sometimes called "dino-fuzz"). These include: *Sinosauropteryx, Caudipteryx, Protarchaeopteryx, Sinornithosaurus, Microraptor* and *Hongshanornis longicresta*.

Sinosauropteryx (whose name means "Chinese dragon feather") was the first of the theropod dinosaurs that was found to have "dino-fuzz". It was about one metre in length and had a very substantial tail with 64 bones. It had hollow leg bones, long legs and short arms (see Figure 6.4). However, there are no clear signs of feathers on this fossil.

The discovery of "dino-fuzz" on this and other theropod dinosaurs has led to considerable speculation about which dinosaurs had feathers. *National Geographic* was so enthusiastic about this that, in one issue, it even published artists' reconstructions of a feathered *Tyrannosaurus rex*.[4]

Caudipteryx was a turkey-sized animal with what seem to be well-preserved feathers. This creature appears to have had feathers on the end of its short tail and symmetrical feathers attached to its very short forelimbs (see Figure 6.5).

Protarchaeopteryx had a tail with a

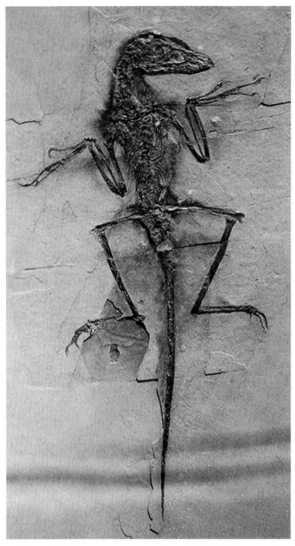

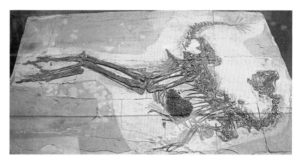

spray of symmetrical feathers. Wing feathers have also been described for this creature. It had long hands – longer than the arms. The legs were long and powerful with three forward-facing toes (see Figure 6.6). This and *Caudipteryx* are reported in detail by Qiang[5] *et al.* and do show evidence of real barbed feathers.

Sinornithosaurus is similar in size to *Sinosauropteryx* and some have argued that it has remains of proto-feathers or feather-like covering (see Figure 6.6).

Microraptor gui has been described as a four-winged dinosaur. The evidence for curved, asymmetric feathers is much clearer on this creature, though they are not as clear as on *Archaeopteryx*, described below. It is described with good close-ups of the feather structures in *Nature*[7]. It appears to have had

Figure 6.8 On the left, a pennaceous feather caught in Dominican amber supposed to be 25 million years old (feather is visible enclosed to the right side of the amber). On the right a pennaceous feather from Archaeopteryx lithographica (von Meyer, 1862[6]). Both are no different to a modern feather.

feathers on all four limbs and is therefore considered by some to be evidence that bird ancestors were gliding creatures that lived in trees, rather than the alternative ground runners. But questions remain about how it managed to fly and how it would get off the ground if it ever landed there (see Figure 6.7). This fossil, however, may simply be an extinct bird.

Hongshanornis longicresta is a fossil that was found in the same Yixian formation in northeastern China where all these Chinese fossils have been discovered. This example has clear evidence of barbed feathers[8], and there is no doubt that it is a bird, since the furcula (wish bone) is visible and the alula feathers on the wing can also be observed (see similar feathers on Archaeopteryx Figure 6.9). Its significance is that this fossil is from similar early Cretaceous rock (the Yixian formation) to the Liaoning shales of the other Chinese finds where some authors are arguing for the development of feathers on dinosaurs.

6.4 Feathers

Feathers, with their sophisticated ridge and hook structure (Case Study 5), are a characteristic feature of birds. When evaluating fossils which have feathers, it is important to determine whether the feathers are asymmetric or symmetric. All flying birds have asymmetric wing or flight feathers, whereas even modern flightless birds generally have symmetric feathers, so it is reasonable to assume that any fossil with asymmetric feathers was a flying creature. Feathers have sometimes been found in amber (hardened tree resin) – an example is shown in Figure 6.8a. This example is estimated to be 25 million years old by conventional dating, and yet there is no indication of development – the feather encased in amber looks just like a modern feather. One can also see that the feather structure is no different in principle to the well preserved *Archaeopteryx* feathers (see Figure 6.8b and 6.9), which are conventionally dated 125 million years older than the amber fossil.

The suggestion that some of the Chinese fossils have proto-feathers has been contested by Feduccia, who described one of the first bird fossils from Liaoning, and is an expert on fossil birds[9]. He and his team studied the evidence and the way in which reptile skin decomposes and looked at fossils of other animals which have "dino-fuzz". They concluded that there is no good evidence that fossilised structures found in China are rudimentary feathers. Instead, the fossilised patterns appear to be "bits of decomposed skin and supporting tissues that just happen to resemble feathers to a modest degree".[10]

The details of feather construction are discussed in detail in Case Study 5.

6.5 Other Fossils

Archaeopteryx

Archaeopteryx was first discovered in 1861 in the Jurassic sediments of the Solnhofen region of Bavaria in Germany. More than one specimen has been found and examination of the skeletal structure of these fossils (see Figure 6.9) shows that this creature lacked the keeled

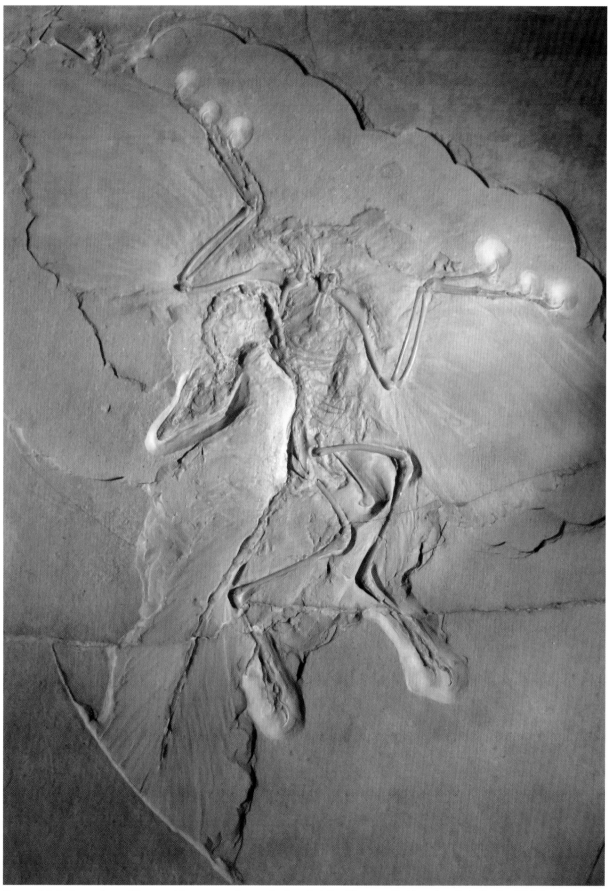

Figure 6.9 Archaeopteryx lithographica – a specimen displayed at the Museum für Naturkunde in Berlin. (This image shows the original fossil - not a cast. Photo: Wikimedia Commons)

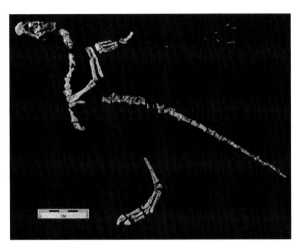

Figure 6.10 A Protoavis fossil found in Triassic rock. (Image from ref 12: Chatterjee S (1991) Cranial anatomy and relationships of a new Triassic bird from Texas. Philosophical Transactions of the Royal Society B: Biological Sciences, 332: 277-346.) (Photo: Wikimedia Commons)

sternum arrangement and the acrocoracoid process which provides the pulley around which the tendon of the supracoracoideus muscle runs and which is necessary for strong flapping flight. Although it did have a furcula, the lack of keeled sternum and acrocoracoid process suggests that it flew by a similar technique to bats, and may have lived in trees. This would be consistent with the evidence that, unlike modern birds, *Archaeopteryx* has no air spaces in its bones, suggesting that it may have been a feathered reptile. Because of the evident fully developed flight feathers, and the fact that shallow sternums are found on modern woodcreepers such as the hoatzin, some think that *Archaeopteryx* was a bird. It was certainly able to fly, even if not very strongly. The brain structure is similar to that of modern birds. Alonso *et al.* carried out a study of endocasts of an *Archaeopteryx* skull and concluded, among other things, that it had an enlarged forebrain with the structural and neurological adaptations, including enhanced somatosensory nerve integration, required for a lifestyle involving flying.[11]

Protoavis

Protoavis (Figure 6.10) is probably the most controversial of the fossil birds. Chatterjee believes it to be a Triassic bird (i.e. 200–250 million years old), much older than *Archaeopteryx*.[12] Only fragments have been found, but its discoverer considers it to have many features associated with flight, for example a keel-like sternum indicating that it would have been a better flyer than *Archaeopteryx*. Its skull was lightly built and pneumatised (that is, it had air-filled cavities), with a temporal region similar to modern birds. It also had a relatively large brain of similar architecture to modern birds, including neurosensory specialisations associated with balance, coordination, flight, agility and high metabolic activity. Claw morphology suggests that *Protoavis* may have been able to climb trees, and Chatterjee has argued that the presence of an acrocoracoid process (the arrangement of bone structure necessary to provide the pulley mechanism used in lifting a wing) indicates that it may have been able to fly.

6.6 Dinosaurs Evolving to Birds?

One of the main contenders in the above list of fossils for a transitional fossil between dinosaurs and birds is *Caudipteryx*. Careful analysis of the anatomy of *Caudipteryx* by Jones *et al.*[13] suggests that it is more like a flightless bird than a dinosaur. These authors concluded that *Caudipteryx* ran using a mechanism more similar to that of modern cursorial birds (running birds) than to typical dinosaurs. The relative hindlimb proportions of *Caudipteryx* are indistinguishable from those of cursorial birds and it was also likely to have had its centre of mass situated towards the front, rather than towards the rear, as in dinosaurs.

An anterior centre of mass is consistent with the short tail of *Caudipteryx*, which is shorter than that of almost all bipedal dinosaurs. Additionally, as in cursorial birds but not dinosaurs, the diminutive tail and the complete absence of a femoral fourth trochanter (a bony lump on the thigh bone to which muscles attach) indicate that the caudofemoralis muscle was not important for locomotion.

Caudipteryx was probably a running bird with a similar lifestyle and morphology to modern ostriches. Other so-called theropod dinosaurs with feathers may also prove to be running birds, albeit with dinosaurian features. Where there is clear evidence of feathers, all fossils can be regarded as birds, either flightless (like *Caudipteryx* and *Protarchaeopteryx*) or able to fly (like *Archaeopteryx*).

Furthermore, as some of the fossils considered above (such as *Hongshanornis longicresta*) are birds, a case could be made that species like *Caudipteryx* and the other Chinese fossils descended from birds rather than *vice versa*, because this is consistent with the sequence of the fossils in the rocks. The Chinese fossils are assumed to be relics of earlier species of bird ancestors because that is consistent with the hypothesis that birds evolved from theropod dinosaurs, not because the evidence demands it.

There are two other difficulties for the accepted theory that birds evolved from theropod dinosaurs. First, the evidence of Triassic "bird-like" footprints[14] in Argentina conflicts with the accepted dogma. Yet the authors of the paper where this was reported preferred to put their faith in the existence of an unknown theropod dinosaur with bird-like feet rather than suggest that these footprints are evidence that birds existed in the Triassic. They reasoned that these could not be bird footprints because they are 100 million years older than the oldest known bird fossils.

This brings us to the second problem for the current theory of bird evolution: *Protoavis*. The fossils of *Protoavis*, while controversial, are consistent with the existence of Triassic birds. Indeed if *Protoavis* was a bird, this would challenge the theory that birds evolved from theropods, whose fossils are 100 million years younger using conventional dating.

6.7 Further Questions

1   Are feathers unique to birds?

2   With true birds found in the same layers as the Chinese Liaoning 'feathered dinosaurs', can the Chinese fossils really represent transitional forms?

3   Are bird-like footprints in the Triassic consistent with a later development of birds from dinosaurs? Think of several explanations, and decide which is most plausible.

Chapter 6 Endnotes

1   Norman D (1991) *Dinosaur!* London: Boxtree Limited p.154

2   Ostrom JH (1970) *Archaeopteryx: Notice of a "new" specimen* Science 170: 537-8

3   Hou L-H, Zhou Z, Martin LD, Feduccia A (1995) *A beaked bird from the Jurassic of China* Nature 377:616-8

4   Sloan CP (1999) *Feathers for T. rex? New birdlike fossils are missing links in dinosaur evolution* National Geographic 196: 98-107

5   Qiang J, Currie PJ, Norell MA, Shu-An J (1998) *Two feathered dinosaurs from northeastern China* Nature 393**:** 753–61 doi:10.1038/31635

6   von Meyer H(1861) *Archaeopteryx litographica (Vogel-Feder) und Pterodactylus von Solenhofen.* Neues Jahrbuch für Mineralogie, Geognosie, Geologie und Petrefakten-Kunde pp. 678–9

7   Xu X, Zhou Z, Wang X, Kuang X, Zhang F, Du X (2003) *Four-winged dinosaurs from China* Nature: 421:335-40 doi:10.1038/nature01342

8   Zhou Z, Zhang F (2005) *Discovery of an ornithurine bird and its implication for early Cretaceous avian radiation* Proceedings of the National Academy of Sciences 102:18998-19002 doi:10.1073/pnas.0507106102

9   Feduccia A, Lingham-Soliar T, Hinchliffe JR (2005) *Do feathered dinosaurs exist? Testing the hypothesis on neontological and paleontological evidence* Journal of Morphology 266:125-66

10   Williamson, D., University of North Carolina Press Release 477 (2005), see: http://www.unc.edu/news/archives/oct05/feducci100705.htm

11   Alonso PD, Milner AC, Ketcham RA, Cookson MJ, Rowe TB (2004) *The avian nature of the brain and inner ear of Archaeopteryx* Nature 430:666-9

12   Chatterjee S (1991) *Cranial anatomy and relationships of a new Triassic bird from Texas* Phil Trans R Soc London 332:277-346

13   Jones TD, Farlow JO, Ruben JA, Henderson DM, Hillenius WJ (2000) *Cursoriality in bipedal archosaurs* Nature 406:716-8 doi:10.1038/35021041

14   Melchor RN, de Valais S, Genise JF (2002) *Bird-like fossil footprints from the late Triassic* Nature 417: 936-8 doi:10.1038/nature00818

CASE STUDY 5:
Intricacies of Bird Flight: Aerodynamics without design?

Most evolutionists take the view that birds evolved from reptiles. What would be involved if this was the case?

Feathers

Feathers are made out of keratin, which is a protein also used to make hair and fingernails. However, there are differences in the exact type of keratin used. Feather keratin occurs in a 'β-sheet' configuration, which differs from the α-helices that generally occur in mammalian keratins.[1] The β keratin of bird feathers is rather like a stretched spring in consistency. The fact that scales of reptiles are also made of keratin is used by some to support the proposal that dinosaurs are the precursors to birds. However, it should be noted that there are significant hurdles to transform one type of keratin to the other.[2] The feather grows from a follicle, and from the central rachis come barbs, which give the vane of the feather (see Figure CS5.1).

Under the microscope the detail becomes clear of the sophistication involved in the barb

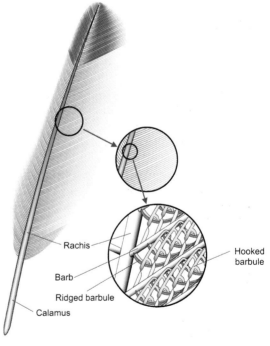

Figure CS5.1 The structure of an asymmetric feather

Rachis
Hooked barbule
Barb
Ridged barbule
Calamus

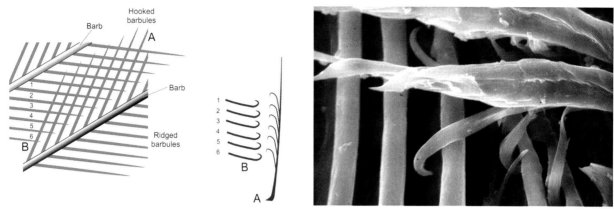

Figure CS5.2 Detail of hook and ridge system for pennaceous feather barbules.
Photograph courtesy of Prof. David Menton, Washington University School of Medicine, St. Louis, Missouri.

system of the pennaceous feather (pennaceous feathers are used for flight, in distinction to plumulaceous, or downy, feathers). In Figure CS5.2 barbules can be seen coming from each barb. They are only visible under the microscope, but have a structure which is essential for feathers to work as aerodynamic surfaces. The barbules in one direction are ridge-like, while the barbules in the opposing direction have hooks. Consequently, the hooks of the barbule in one direction grip the ridges of the opposing barbules and slide over them. Figure CS5.2 shows further detail of this remarkable arrangement. Thus adjacent barbs are held together by a microscopic sliding mechanism in between each barb.

Breathing Systems of Reptiles and Birds

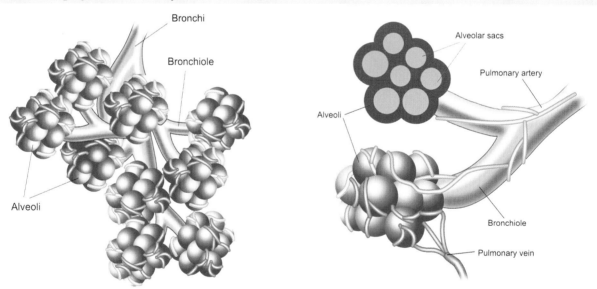

Figure CS5.3 End-flow mass exchange in mammalian and reptilian respiration.

Another remarkable feature of birds is the way they breathe. This is entirely different from both mammals and most reptiles, which use a diaphragm and a 'single-pass' ventilating apparatus. That system brings the air to a halt after it is inhaled, before being exhaled at the second part of the cycle. However, birds have a 'two-pass' system where the air is in continuous transit through the lung.

Gas exchange in the respiratory system in the reptilian and mammalian lungs is provided by an end-flow exchange system (see Figure CS5.3). The gas exchange takes place across the membranes of small balloon-like structures (called alveoli) attached to the branches of the bronchial passages. Oxygen

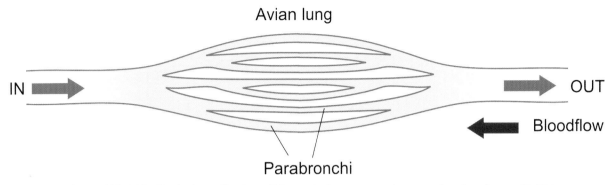

Avian lung

IN →

OUT →

Bloodflow ←

Parabronchi

Figure CS5. 4 Idealised schematic of parallel counterflow mass exchange system in avian respiration

and carbon dioxide are exchanged as these alveoli inflate and deflate with inhalation and exhalation. But, in contrast to this, the bird lung (Figure CS5.4) is a parallel flow system, where, instead of alveoli, the bronchial passage breaks into tubes known as parabronchi so that oxygen is continuously flowing through the lung.

It is significant that such a mass exchange system is used for a bird, since the breathing of a bird is much faster than in a mammal or land-based reptile. It is well known in engineering that a mass exchanger is at its most efficient when a counterflow system is in use. In more specific terms, the most efficient system for diffusing gas across a membrane

from one fluid to another is when the fluids flow in opposite directions[3]. It is this principle that is being used in the respiratory system of the avian lung, which is effectively a series of counterflow mass exchangers between the blood flowing in one direction and the air flowing in the other. Consequently, this uses a minimal amount of tissue to achieve a given rate of gas exchange. The energy involved in inhalation and exhalation is also minimised.

Not only is the mass exchange system entirely different in birds from that in reptiles and mammals, but the ventilatory pathways[4] are also totally different in construction (Figure CS5.5).

A bird has no diaphragm, unlike mammals

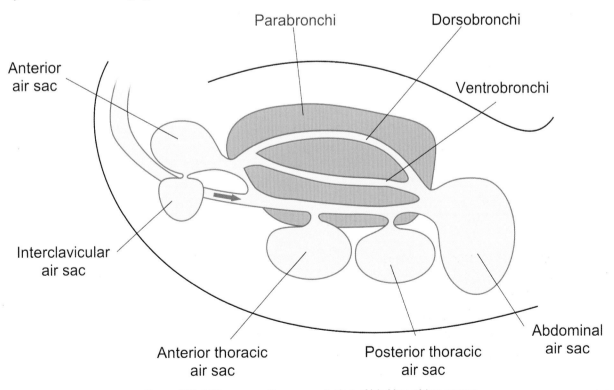

Parabronchi

Dorsobronchi

Anterior air sac

Ventrobronchi

Interclavicular air sac

Anterior thoracic air sac

Posterior thoracic air sac

Abdominal air sac

Figure CS5.5 Diagrammatic representation of bird breathing system

and reptiles (including crocodiles and alligators, which, as noted below, even though they may have unidirectional breathing, do have a diaphragm). Instead it uses the sternum (breastbone) to move air round the circulatory system. During inhalation, the sternum (breastbone) moves forward and downward with a combined movement of the vertebral ribs such that the internal pressure is lowered and the rear (posterior) and front (anterior) air sacs inflate in succession. Air from the trachea and bronchial pathways moves into the rear air sacs and, simultaneously, air from the lungs moves into the front air sacs. During exhalation, the reverse happens. The sternum moves backward and the pressure is increased,

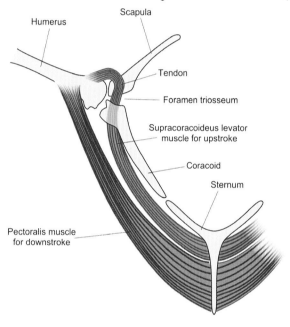

causing the front and rear air sacs to deflate. Air from the rear sacs moves into the lungs and, simultaneously, air from the front sacs moves into the trachea and out of the body. Consequently, air circulates unidirectionally through the lungs with two cycles of inhalation and exhalation taking one packet of air through the system. The first inhalation takes air to the rear air sac. Then at the first exhalation the movement of air causes that packet of air to pass through the lung. The second inhalation then draws the same packet of air into the front air sac, and finally the second exhalation drives this packet of air out of the trachea. Then the two-stage cycle is repeated.

Recently evidence has come to light that crocodilians may also breathe using a "single-pass" ventilating system[5]. However, it is important to note that crocodilians still have the hepatic piston mechanism of breathing, which birds do not have, and crocodiles do not have pneumaticity (that is they do not have air sacs and hollow bones). Put simply, crocodilians may have unidirectional breathing but with a diaphragm and no air sacs. Thus these findings, rather than providing a link between reptile breathing and bird breathing, actually suggest there is little connection between the two systems and that both are unique in function.

A further remarkable fact is that specialised articulated joints in vertebral and sternal ribs of birds are required to facilitate the dorso–ventral movement of the posterior part of the sternum during lung ventilation.[6] This means that the rib cage of a bird is articulated to enable it to swivel back and forth between the spine and the ventral cavity. No intermediate stage in the development of such an articulated system of rib cage joints has ever been found in extant reptiles or in the fossil record.

Figure CS5.6 View end-on of the sternum (breast-bone) in a bird. The supracoracoideus muscle is (uniquely to birds) attached to the keel of the sternum bone and threaded through the coracoid, across the foramen triosseum, and over the scapula so that, on contraction, it lifts the humerus (arm bone), and thus the wing. This is a powerful pulley-like system for the upstroke action in flight. For the downstroke the pectoralis major muscle (main breast muscle) is contracted. There is a muscle in reptiles identified as a 'rudimentary' supracoracoideus (see Figure CS5.7), but its action is totally different.

Supracoracoideus Muscle and Hole in the Coracoid Bone

The sternum bone used for breathing is also crucial for the flight muscle arrangement. Across the keel of the sternum is the pectoralis major muscle which powers the downstroke of a bird's wings. But very important also is

the smaller supracoracoideus muscle, which has a tendon which acts like a hoist over a pulley. It is anchored to the keel of the sternum beneath, and attaches to the main humerus (arm bone) from above (see Figure CS5.6), so

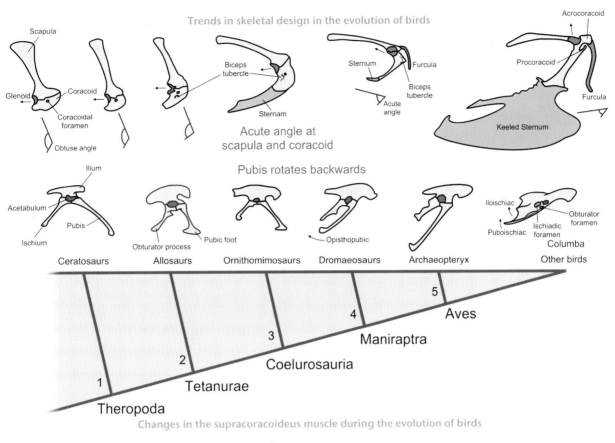

Trends in skeletal design in the evolution of birds

Acute angle at scapula and coracoid

Pubis rotates backwards

Changes in the supracoracoideus muscle during the evolution of birds

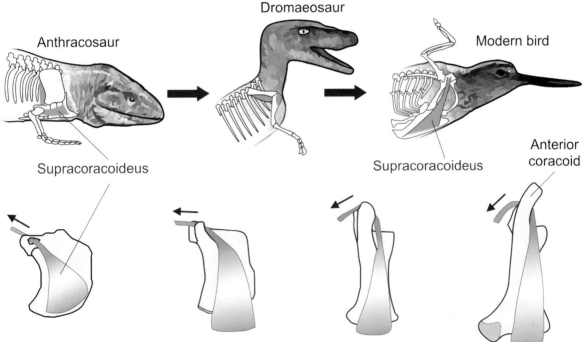

Anterior coracoid elongates and acquires a 'foramen'. Suoracoracoideus muscle moves too and travels through foramen. Muscle becomes a levator.

Archaeopteryx ➡ Hypothetical intermediates ➡ Modern birds

Figure CS5.7 Typical diagrams appearing in textbooks showing the development of the bone and muscle arrangement to change a tetrapod ancestor to a modern bird. The evidence for any of these structural changes is completely absent in the fossil record.

that on contraction, it pulls the humerus bone upwards. The supracoracoideus muscle thus gives power for the upstroke and also rotates the humerus at the peak of the upstroke. The multifunctioning arrangement of the sternum ensures that there is no wastage of weight and that breathing in flight is thus coupled with the wing dynamics.

The astonishing fact concerning the bird's supracoracoideus muscle is that the tendon of this muscle is actually threaded through the coracoid bone and reaches across the foramen triosseum gap, then over the scapula, before finally attaching to the humerus bone from above. In bats, the equivalent muscle (the pectoralis minor) is simply inserted into the coracoid bone and thus plays no part in elevating the wing.[7] Bats pull the wing up by using muscles overlying the shoulder blade and back, but without the keeled sternum and the pulley arrangement of birds, they cannot normally take off from the ground into the air.

The main contender for a transitional creature leading to birds is *Archaeopteryx*, the fossils of which are found in Bavaria in southern Germany – one well preserved example is from the Solnhofen quarry. Examination of the skeletal structure of these fossils shows that this creature lacked the keeled sternum arrangement and the acrocoracoid process which provides the pulley around which the tendon of the supracoracoideus muscle runs. Consequently, it is more than likely that it flew by a similar technique to bats and may have lived in trees, particularly as, unlike modern birds, the archaeopteryx has no evidence of air spaces in its bones. This suggests that, possibly, it may have been a feathered reptile. As Sodera notes[8], the only significant feature in common with birds is its feathers. However, this is not evidence that birds evolved from reptiles, since there is no compelling reason to say that birds were the only creatures that had feathers. Others take the view that the archaeopteryx was a bird because of the fully developed flight feathers. Either way, what is clear is that it is certainly not transitional in terms of the advanced pennaceous flight feathers.

The other contenders for transitional fossils to birds are some recent discoveries in China of dinosaur fossils as discussed in Chapter 6 (such as *Sinornithosaurus*) with skin from which emanate fibrous structures, which it has been suggested were feathers. Some of these Chinese fossils such as *Hongshanornis longicresta* have a furcula (wish-bone) as found in birds in front of the sternum. They also have recognisable feathers, and there is no doubt therefore that they are birds which now are extinct. The furcula bone replaces the two collar bones (clavicles) found in other reptiles (and mammals). *Caudipteryx*, *Microraptor gui* and *Protarcheopteryx,* which show evidence of some barbed feathers (as discussed in Chapter 6), could well be extinct flightless birds. Two points need to be noted concerning these Chinese specimens. First, none of the fibrous structures in the fossils have been convincingly shown to be examples of intermediate transitional "proto-feathers". Secondly, there is no evidence of any evolutionary development of a supracoracoideus pulley arrangement in these specimens. Either one has it, as in *Hongshanornis longicresta* (which is clearly a bird), or it is absent. There is no intermediate acrocoracoid arrangement preserved in the fossil record, as one might expect for the evolutionary development of flapping flight. In general, the creatures with neither furcula nor keeled sternum (such as the Chinese Liaoning shale dinosaur fossils like *Sinornithosaurus*) are also the ones which clearly do not have feathers either (as against extinct birds such as *Hongshanornis longicresta* which had both).[9]

In reptiles, the forelimb muscle arrangement is indeed connected to the humerus (unlike in bats, where it is connected directly into the coracoid). Reptiles do also have a supracoracoideus, but it is nothing like the sophisticated arrangement involving the acrocoracoid process that birds have. In alligators, for instance, the supracoracoideus originates on the coracoid and inserts onto the deltopectoral crest of the humerus, and aids in shoulder flexion and in drawing the arm forward. Consequently, the reptile supracoracoideus has been taken as indicative that reptiles must be ancestral to birds. But, in reality, diagrams like those in Figure CS5.7 have simply been worked out in textbooks to give the impression to the unsuspecting reader that a gradual origin of the keeled sternum along with the threaded supracoracoideus arrangement is possible. Evidence is completely absent in the fossil record to support any of these supposed developments from reptiles to birds. The evidence itself suggests that the design and morphology of birds are fundamentally different from that of any other creatures.

Further Questions

1   What are the different types of feathers that are found on birds?

2   What structure of barbs and barbules in feathers is found at the microscopic level?

3   Using this structure, how do adjacent barbs of bird feathers attach to each other? Does this support a design thesis?

4   What unique features are found in the avian lung and respiration system?

5   What muscle is used for upward wing movement and how is the ligament attached to the humerus bone?

Case Study 5 Endnotes

1   Bonser RHC, Saker L, Jeronimidis G (2004) *Toughness anisotropy in feather keratin* Journal of Materials Science 39:2895-6 Also see website of Richard Bonser at http://www.rdg.ac.uk/biomim/personal/richard/keratin.htm which has a useful summary of the material properties of feathers

2   Alexander NJ (1970) *Comparison of α and β keratin in reptiles* Cell and Tissue Research 110:153-65

3   Incropera FP, DeWitt DP, Bergman DL, Lavine AS (2006) *Fundamentals of Heat and Mass Transfer* Sixth Edition Wiley: London, New York

4   A helpful summary of bird respiration is given at the following web-site http://people.eku.edu/ritchisong/birdrespiration.html.

5   Farmer CG, Sanders K (2010) *Unidirectional Airflow in the Lungs of Alligators* Science 327:338-40

6   Quick DE, Ruben JA (2009) *Cardio-Pulmonary Anatomy in Theropod Dinosaurs: Implications From Extant Archosaurs* Journal of Morphology 270:1232–46

7   Sodera V (2003) *One small speck to man* Vij Sodera Productions pp. 237-56 and available at website: www.onesmallspeck.com

8   Sodera op cit. 238

9   McIntosh AC (2009) *Evidence of design in bird feathers and avian respiration* Int J of Design & Nature and Ecodynamics 4:154–69

Chapter 7
The Origin of the Mammals

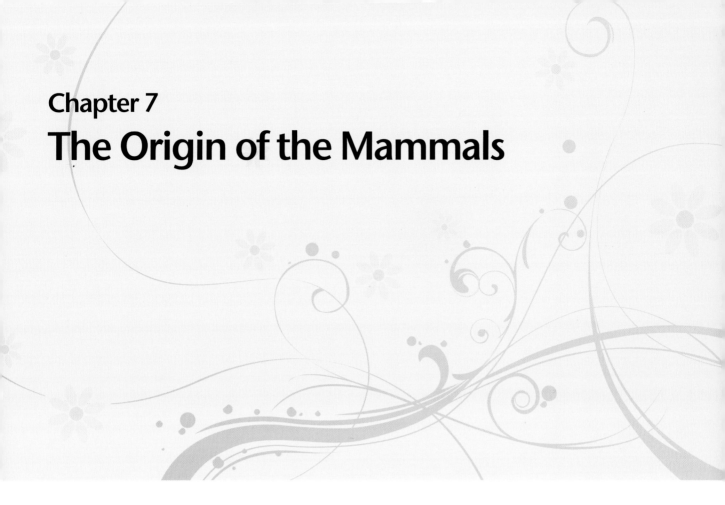

7.1 Mammal-like Reptiles

Donald Prothero, Professor of Geology at Occidental College in Los Angeles and Lecturer in Geobiology at the California Institute of Technology in Pasadena, has written:

> Another excellent example of a transitional sequence is the evolution of mammals from their ancestors, the synapsids. These were once called "mammal-like reptiles", but that term is no longer used because synapsids are not reptiles - the two groups evolved in parallel from a common ancestor.[1]

Synapsids are a classification construct (i.e. clade) that includes so-called mammal-like reptiles and true mammals. The non-mammalian synapsids comprise the pelycosaurs, which are regarded as primitive, and the therapsids, which are regarded as more advanced. In contradistinction, the sauropsids are tetrapod animals including reptiles, dinosaurs and birds. Together, the synapsids and the sauropsids comprise the amniotes, all of which are characterised by the presence of amniotic membranes surrounding the embryo, either within an egg or within the body of the mother. These embryonic membranes distinguish the amniotes from the amphibians, which lay their eggs in water and generally possess a distinctive larval stage in their life history.

Prior to the 1990s, the non-mammalian synapsids were actually considered true reptiles. Then a revised evolutionary classification was widely adopted and these extinct creatures were no longer considered reptiles but were regarded as the ancestors of mammals. Why is this? Prothero gives us a clue:

> In this instance, we have hundreds of beautiful fossils of skulls as well as many complete skeletons that document the transition over 100 million years from the late Carboniferous to the early Jurassic ... Among the striking evolutionary

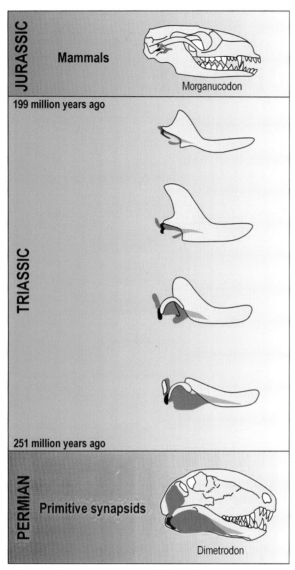

JURASSIC

Mammals

Morganucodon

199 million years ago

TRIASSIC

251 million years ago

PERMIAN

Primitive synapsids

Dimetrodon

Figure 7.1 Proposed Synapsid Transition according to conventional dating methods

changes occurring in the synapsids was in their lower jaws. Most reptiles have several bones in the lower jaw, and Dimetrodon shares this characteristic. But mammals have only a single lower jawbone, the dentary. Throughout synapsid evolution, we see the gradual reduction of the non-dentary elements of the jaw as they are crowded towards the back and eventually lost. The dentary bone, in contrast, gets larger and takes over the entire jaw. In the final stage of evolution, the dentary bone expands until it makes direct contact with the skull and develops a new articulation with it.[1]

This transitional sequence is almost solely based on changes in cranial architecture, which is distinctively different between reptiles and mammals. In particular, in mammals, the lower jaw comprises a single dentary bone whereas in reptiles, the lower jaw consists of many. It is suggested that some of these many bones eventually became the bones of the mammalian middle ear:

> Where did the rest of the non-dentary bones go? Most were lost, but the articular bone and the corresponding quadrate bone of the skull are now the malleus ("hammer") and incus ("anvil") bones in your middle ear. This may seem bizarre until you realise that most reptiles hear with their lower jaws, transmitting sound from this to the middle ear through the jaw articulation.[1]

Figure 7.1 (accurately redrawn here from that shown in *New Scientist*) is lacking in some important details. We have *Dimetrodon*, a "primitive" synapsid found in Permian strata and we have the mammal *Morganucodon*, found in the Jurassic. The reader of the *New Scientist* article, however, has no idea what the intermediate jaws represent as they are not named. Also the suggestion that mammals are only found in Jurassic strata is highly misleading.

For example, *Adelobasileus cromptoni* as well as *Morganucodon* itself have been found in the Triassic, as Prothero himself later acknowledges.

Prothero then makes a remarkable statement that the general reader has little choice but to take at face value:

> In addition, during embryonic development, the middle ear bones start in the lower jaw, and then eventually migrate to the ear.

In mammalian embryos, however, the middle ear ossicles (bones) are derived from the 1st and 2nd arch mesenchyme (i.e. embryonic connective tissue of mesodermal origin). The embryonic evidence seems to be simply misinterpreted.

7.2 Pelycosaurs

The primitive synapsid *Dimetrodon* is probably the most common example of a pelycosaur. A diagram of its skull is shown in Figure 7.2.

This animal is regarded as somewhat mammal-like, thanks to the presence of teeth that enabled it to "chew" its prey, aiding ingestion. Modern-day carnivorous reptiles generally "gulp" their prey whole. Chewing demands specialised teeth and the jaw muscles to go with them, and is characteristic of animals that primarily eat plants. Remarkably, however, some true reptiles also have teeth, including many dinosaur species that were herbivorous. The crucial point to note is the relative sizes of the dentary and surangular bones of the lower jaw. The surangular bone is greatly reduced in the herbivore. So where does that leave the jaw (and the diet) of "mammal-like" synapsids such as *Dimetrodon*? Although this animal is considered to have been carnivorous with large, powerful jaws, it also had two types of teeth: sharp canines and shearing teeth. It appears that these creatures

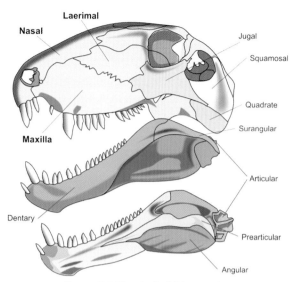

Figure 7.2 The skull of Dimetrodon

could also "chew" their food and so may be more correctly classified as omnivores. Their jaw architecture would need to support the musculature required for chewing.

However, not all pelycosaurs are regarded as carnivorous. The Caseidae and the Edaphosauridae were probably true herbivores. A typical herbivorous

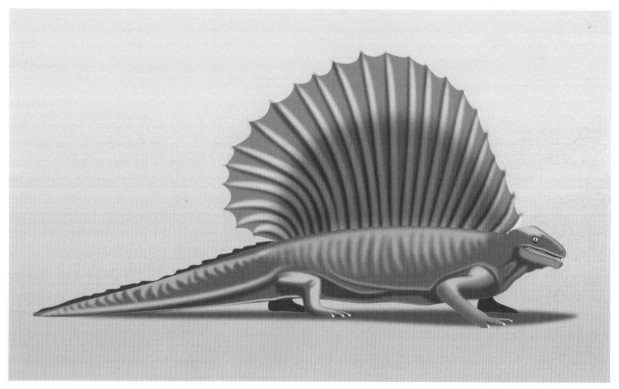

Figure 7.3 Edaphosaurus

pelycosaur is *Edaphosaurus*. The popular BBC series *Walking with Monsters* describes the carnivorous *Dimetrodon* attacking the herbivorous *Edaphosaurus*. Whether this ever happened is, of course, speculation. What is more certain is that both *Dimetrodon* and *Edaphosaurus* were cold-blooded creatures that used their sails to capture heat from the sun (see Figure 7.3). They are mainly distinguishable by close examination of their skulls.

7.3 Therapsids

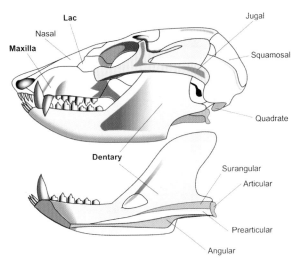

Figure 7.4 The skull of a Cynodont

The other main group of non-mammalian synapsids was the therapsids, which are also to be found in middle Permian strata. The therapsids include three major clades, the dinocephalians, the herbivorous anomodonts and the mostly carnivorous theriodonts, which include the gorgonopsids. The latter have been popular in natural history documentaries such as *Walking with Monsters* and the ITV series *Primeval*.

Therapsids were small to moderate-sized animals with several mammalian skeletal characteristics, such as fewer bones in the skull than the other reptiles, differentiated teeth (incisors, canines, and cheek teeth) and a bony palate which permitted breathing while chewing. From a skeletal perspective, the most mammal-like therapsids were the cynodonts. A representative skull of a cynodont (*Probainognathus*) is shown in Figure 7.4.

According to Prothero:

In the Triassic and early Jurassic, the protomammal story culminated in the most advanced of all the synapsids, the cynodonts. They had a mammal-like posture, a fully developed secondary palate, a large temporal opening for multiple sets of jaw muscles allowing complex chewing movements, and highly specialised molars and premolars for grinding and chewing. Some of them probably had hair. Many of the later species of cynodonts are so mammal-like that it has long been controversial as to where to draw the line between true mammals and the rest of the synapsids. The oldest fossils that palaeontologists now agree are mammals come from the late Triassic. They were shrew-sized, with a fully developed joint between the dentary bone and the skull, and three middle-ear bones. Thanks to the fossil record, we have a full picture of how they evolved from synapsids.

To suggest that we now have a full picture of how mammals evolved from synapsids is an overstatement. Thus far, we (and the Professor) have only considered aspects of mammalian skeletal characteristics that can be inferred from the direct examination of synapsid fossil remains. Relative proportions of the cranial bones such as the dentary and postdentary, for example, can only indicate one aspect of this presumed transition.

7.4 An Alternative View

Not every palaeontologist would agree with Prothero's evolutionary assessment of the synapsid cranial morphology. The most recent review has been written by Christian Sidor.[2]

This article presents detailed findings based on the morphological analysis of an extensive number of fossil synapsid jaws. These included 19 pelycosaurs, six basal therapsids, 13 dinocephalians, 25 anomodonts, 10 gorgonopsians, 10 therocephalians and 25 cynodonts. His conclusions are as follows:

1. The lack of a well-supported phylogeny [i.e. tree of evolutionary relationships] has allowed exaggerated estimates of morphological convergence or parallelism in the synapsid fossil record. The hypothesis of multiple therapsid groups arising independently from pelycosaur-grade ancestors necessitated rampant homoplasy[3] and is now considered untenable.

2. Despite the striking differences between the lower jaws of basal synapsids [i.e. pelycosaurs] and mammals, jaw evolution within synapsids was predominantly conservative. Except for dicynodont anomodonts, most therapsids do not acquire substantial morphological novelty in their lower jaw structure.

3. When comparing the dentary and postdentary bones with overall jaw length, the changes in body-size are not sufficient to explain the reduction of the postdentary bones in synapsid evolution. Importantly, when compared with other synapsid subgroups, cynodonts are characterised by smaller-than-predicted postdentary areas.

4. Selection acting to decrease the size of the postdentary bones, and thereby improving high-frequency hearing, is still the most tenable mechanism for the evolution of the mammalian lower jaw. However, this hypothesis leads to difficulties in explaining the converse pattern in anomodont therapsids (i.e. the decreasing size of the dentary and increasing size of the postdentary bones).

5. These conclusions, in combination with those of recent studies on long-term patterns of limb and cranial evolution, suggest that morphological trends within synapsids should be re-investigated within a quantitative and phylogenetic framework.

In other words, the most detailed recent review suggests that there is little supporting evidence for the transitional sequence proposed by Prothero and others. But this is just the beginning of the problems concerning the emergence of mammalian characteristics in the fossil record.

7.5 When is a Mammal a Mammal?

According to T.S. Kemp:

> The formal definition of Mammalia is simple as far as the living mammals are concerned, because of the large number of unique characters they possess. However, the fossil record makes the situation a good deal less clear cut.[4]

Kemp discusses the difficulty in assigning mammal-likeness to organisms that do not possess many relevant features. For example, pelycosaurs have very few mammalian characters, just a small temporal fenestra [a small opening usually covered with membrane] in the skull and an enlarged canine tooth in the jaw. Furthermore, Kemp goes on to suggest:

> An arbitrary decision is made about which characters to select as defining characters, and therefore which particular node on the stem lineage to label Mammalia. *Characters deemed appropriate are those reflecting the evolution of the fundamental mammalian biology* [emphasis added]. The essence of mammalian life is to be found in their endothermic [warm-blooded] temperature physiology, greatly enlarged brain, dentition capable of chewing food, highly agile, energetic locomotion, and so on. The organisms that achieved this grade of overall organisation

are deemed to be Mammalia, and consequently those characters that they possess are the defining characters of the group.[5]

Of these attributes, only certain skeletal characteristics can be presented as evidence from the fossil record, but, as Kemp has already indicated, there are many other significant features of mammals. These include: (1) the possession of a relatively large brain and highly sensitive sense organs, (2) characteristic growth and development patterns, (3) endothermic temperature physiology with high metabolic rates, insulation and high respiratory rates, (4) turbinal bones and a secondary palate, and (5) precise osmoregulatory and chemoregulatory mechanisms.

The obsession with defining clades like Mammalia precisely is curious in the evolutionary paradigm, where no boundaries to variation among kinds are expected and any definition should be as arbitrary as the distinction between "hill" and "mountain".

1. The brain

According to Kemp, there is little consensus about the evolution of the brain within the cynodonts, the most mammal-like of all the synapsids. Some have suggested that the brain of the cynodont was very small compared to that of mammals, although others think that there may have been some enlargement. However, Kemp goes on:

> What is beyond dispute, however, is that the earliest mammals themselves did have significantly enlarged brains... the brain size in Mesozoic mammals lay within the lower part of the size range of the brains of living mammals. This represents an overall increase of some four or more times the volume of basal amniote brains, and presumably involved the evolution of the neocortex, the complex, six layered surface of the cerebral hemispheres that is one of the most striking of all mammalian characters.[6]

2. Growth and development

The pattern of growth of amniotes other than mammals is described as indeterminate. This means it is continuous throughout life and there is no standard adult size. This pattern of growth is associated with successive replacements of each tooth (polyphyodonty) providing an increased size and number of teeth concomitant with growth. In mammals, however, growth is described as determinate. There is rapid growth in the juvenile leading to a characteristically-sized mature adult. This unique characteristic of mammals is also associated with a small number of tooth replacements (diphyodonty). For example, human milk teeth are shed to be replaced (just once) with the permanent adult dentition. According to Kemp:

> It is not until the basal mammal Morganucodon that the combination of determinate growth and diphyodonty is known to have evolved... The incisors, canines, and anterior postcanines are replaced once, and posterior postcanines are added sequentially at the back, not replaced, and therefore can properly be referred to as molar teeth. Given its correlation with growth pattern, it is assumed by this stage that lactation had evolved.[7]

In other words, there is no fossil evidence for the emergence of determinate growth and diphyodonty until the first true mammal appears in the fossil record. This fact is omitted in most accounts of mammal evolution.

3. Temperature physiology

According to Kemp:

> Nothing is more fundamental to the life of mammals than their endothermic temperature physiology, if only because it entails a 10-fold increase in daily food requirements. Such a huge cost must be balanced by an equally large benefit for endothermy to have evolved

and been maintained. Yet surprisingly there is no consensus about exactly how, why, or when endothermy evolved in the course of the evolution of the mammals. The fact that the birds share a virtually identical mode of endothermic temperature physiology with the mammals adds little elucidation: the same contentious issues apply to them. The problem arises because of the complex nature of endothermy. It has two distinct primary functions in modern mammals, and it also involves a considerable array of structures and processes, including a regulating system for the high metabolic rate, variable conductivity of the skin by use of hair and cutaneous capillaries, neurological mechanisms for bringing about panting and shivering, and so on.

In endotherms, body temperature must be controlled with extreme accuracy. This is done by maintaining a body temperature which is significantly higher than that of the environment, thanks to a high metabolic rate together with effective insulation. In addition, it is necessary to have fine control over heat loss by vasodilatation (enlarging) and vasoconstriction (narrowing) of the skin capillaries. Emergency measures must be in place for extreme conditions, such as the ability to pant, sweat or shiver. According to Kemp:

> The adaptive significance of a constant body temperature is hard to describe succinctly because it so permeates the total biological organisation of a mammal.

Needless to say, there have been various hypotheses regarding the timing of the appearance of endothermy in synapsids, although according to Kemp they do not stand up to close scrutiny. The best evidence would be the discovery of insulation such as fur. Prothero suggests that some synapsids "probably had hair" but this is no more than wishful thinking. Unfortunately for him, the fossil record does not provide the necessary evidence. According to Kemp:

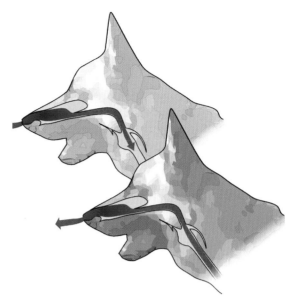

Figure 7.5 Turbinal Bones in Mammals

... as yet no mammal like reptile has been shown by direct fossil evidence to have possessed a pelt.[8]

4. Turbinal bones and a secondary palate

In modern mammals, the turbinal bones inside the nasal cavity play an important role in endothermy. These very thin bones are covered in epithelium serving two functions, namely, chemoreception (an acute sense of taste and smell) and to warm and humidify incoming air (see Figure 7.5). Turbinal bones have never been found in any mammal-like reptile, although, in some cases, fine bony ridges could be sites of attachment for putative cartilaginous turbinals. The presence of a secondary palate in some synapsids might indicate endothermy but it is also present in modern crocodiles to assist with their semi-aquatic lifestyle.

5. Osmoregulation and chemoregulation

Mammals are able to regulate their internal chemical environment by using the kidney tubule to create hyperosmotic urine. Concentrating the urine allows mammals to use soluble urea as their prime nitrogen-excreting molecule without excessive water loss. The kidney mechanism adjusts the balance between reabsorption and secretion of water and is under precise hormonal control to maintain blood plasma at an optimal composition.

Conclusion

Taken together, all of these facets of mammalian life present a vastly more complex picture than that presented in Prothero's *New Scientist* article. The problem is summed up by Kemp as follows:

> Seen in this light, there is no identifiable, single key adaptation or innovation of mammals because each and every one of the processes and structures is an essential part of the whole organism's organisation. To regard for example endothermy, or a large brain, or juvenile care as somehow more fundamental is arbitrarily to focus on one point in an interdependent network of causes and effects. Endothermy is necessary for maintained elevated levels of aerobic activity, but the activity itself is simultaneously essential for collecting

7.6 Horse Evolution

The fossil record of horses has often featured in the scientific debate about origins, with many biologists regarding it as important evidence in support of evolutionary theory. For instance, the textbook *Biological Sciences* states:

> The horse provides one of the best examples of evolutionary history (phylogeny) based on an almost complete fossil record found in North American sedimentary deposits from the early Eocene to the present.[10]

In this section we review the horse series as it is generally portrayed in textbooks and museum exhibits and consider its role as supportive evidence for evolutionary theory.

A brief description of the horse series

The consensus sequence regarding the

enough food to sustain the high metabolic rate. The large brain causes high levels of learning and social behaviour, but the latter are necessary for the parental care that allows the offspring time to develop the large brain in the first place. Lactation is on the one hand necessary for mammalian development, yet on the other can only exist by virtue of the high metabolic rates and efficient food collection. Which has ontological priority?[9]

There is no doubt that the so-called synapsid transition leading to the emergence of mammals is regarded by neo-Darwinists as the best evidence that the fossil record has to offer. Nevertheless, the speculations based upon fossil material cannot and do not begin to address the origin of the unique structural, biochemical and physiological characteristics that define all mammals (not to mention their genetic basis). We suggest that teachers and students at least reflect upon these other fundamental aspects of mammalian life when considering the supposed emergence of mammals from the synapsids.

evolution of the horse is shown in Figure 7.6.

According to current thinking, the root of the family tree of the horse is to be found in a creature called *Hyracotherium* or *Eohippus* (dawn horse), whose fossils are known from the Lower Eocene deposits of North America and Europe. *Hyracotherium* was a small mammal with four toes on the front feet and three on the rear. It had low-crowned teeth. Its characteristics are those of a forest-dwelling animal that browsed on foliage.

Mesohippus (or *Oligohippus*), a sheep-sized Oligocene form, had only three toes on the forefoot. As in *Hyracotherium*, the teeth were low-crowned. *Mesohippus* appears to have become extinct by the middle Oligocene, and is thought to have given rise to the characteristic Miocene genus *Merychippus*.

Merychippus also had three toes, but the central one apparently bore most of the weight. The structure of the foot suggests that

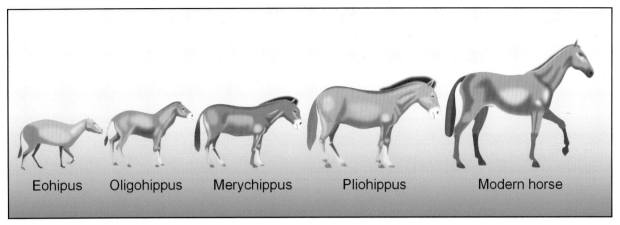

Figure 7.6 General consensus sequence for the evolution of the horse

a strong elastic ligament, like that of modern horses, passed behind this central toe. Unlike *Hyracotherium* and *Mesohippus*, the teeth of this horse were high-crowned, coated in cement, and had a more complex chewing surface.

It is thought that a branch from the *Merychippus* line led to *Pliohippus*, a late Miocene to Pliocene form. In *Pliohippus* the side toes became vestigial – although some species are now known to have had three toes. The teeth were high-crowned. A descendant of *Pliohippus* probably gave rise to the Pleistocene genus *Equus*, which rapidly spread to Europe, Asia, Africa, and South America. However, by the end of the Pleistocene the genus was extinct in the New World. Nine species survive to this day in the Old World – the wild Asian horse, four species of asses, and four zebras.

The major trends of horse evolution

It is common to find this story presented with diagrams illustrating what are considered to be the major trends of horse evolution (increased body size, reduction of side toes, increased height of teeth). In one sense, these trends are indeed real. There is a trend towards the loss of toes from four on the forefoot and three on the hindfoot of Hyracotherium (4/3), to 3/3 in Mesohippus, and 1/1 in Equus. There is also a trend towards increased height of teeth; all pre-Miocene horses were low-crowned, and crown heights increase from Merychippus to

Equus. However, the textbook diagrams often make these trends look much more gradual and unidirectional than they really are in the fossil record.

Take, for instance, the increase in body size which is one of the most striking trends in popular presentations of the horse series. In fact, the increase in size between *Hyracotherium* and *Equus* was by no means gradual, constant, or progressive. An analysis by MacFadden (1987) of 24 supposed ancestral-descendant species pairs revealed that 19 showed body-size increases. However, the remaining five lineages showed size *decreases*. There are even lineages within the horse family tree that show size decreases followed by reversals back to increased size. [11,12,13]

The family tree of the horse is more like a branching bush than a single straight trunk. Popular presentations that suggest a simple, gradual and progressive straight-line of evolution from *Hyracotherium* to *Equus* are not supported by the actual fossil data. Most evolutionary scientists now acknowledge that this is the case. For instance, in *Biological Science*, it is stated:

> The history of the horse does not show a gradual transition regularly spaced in time and locality, and neither is the fossil record totally complete. [14]

Similarly, the textbook *Advanced Biology* states:

...palaeontologists believe that there were numerous complications. For one thing, the rate at which evolution took place was probably not uniform, but sporadic and irregular. For another, there are thought to have been times when certain of the trends were reversed when, for instance, horses became smaller for a while.[15]

Evidence for evolutionary change?

Of course, none of this confounds the evolutionary interpretation of the series; it is merely that textbooks and museum displays are simplistic, portraying only selected trends. They do not reflect all the twists, turns, offshoots, and dead-ends that are evident in the fossil record. However, the horse series is also perfectly consistent with a non-evolutionary explanation of the development of life.

There is a common misconception that scientists who reject evolutionary theory must believe that species are fixed and unchangeable.

The family tree of the horse is more like a branching bush than a single straight trunk.

That is incorrect: non-evolutionary scientists accept that species can change, but they believe that biological change has natural limits.

The most developed non-evolutionary model is based on the concept of Basic Types. A Basic Type is a distinct group of organisms that originated separately from other Basic Types, which cannot be traced back to a universal common ancestor. Rather than a single evolutionary tree, this entails an "orchard" of trees. Nevertheless, each Basic Type is a broad group probably encompassing many species. While each Basic Type originated separately, a great deal of variation has occurred within the created group. For instance, all dogs – including wolves, coyotes, jackals, dingos and domestic dogs – probably belong to the same Basic Type. However, dogs are distinctly different from, and unrelated to, other groups (e.g. cats, bears, weasels).

Basic Type biology, pioneered by Professor Siegfried Scherer and colleagues in Germany, seeks to identify the original Basic Types using hybridisation (cross-breeding) studies.[16] Scientists in the USA have suggested additional criteria for identifying and classifying the Basic Types, some of which can also be applied to fossil organisms.[17] This has developed into an exciting field of biological study with its own conferences and publications.

The Basic Type concept has been applied to horses, both living and extinct forms.[18,19,20] These studies suggest that all horses, including the 150 or so fossil species, are probably related in a single Basic Type. The ancestors of these horses probably possessed latent (i.e. unexpressed) genetic information that gave the horse type tremendous potential for variety. One way in which this latent genetic potential may be regulated is by differential gene expression. By this we mean that in living organisms there are mechanisms by which genes can be turned on (expressed) or turned off (repressed). For example, horses may have a genetic "switch" that determines whether they develop side toes. Other regulatory genes may control body size, shape of the teeth, and so on.

Variation occurs within groups, such as dogs (Photo: Tambako the Jaguar/Flickr)

Consistent with this theory, there is evidence for differential gene expression in modern horses. Ewart (1894) studied horse embryos and found that at an early stage of development tiny limb buds appeared beneath the splint bones.[21] When he dissected these buds to determine their internal structure he found that they resembled toes, with caps at the end that he believed represented hooves. At the most advanced stage it was even possible to distinguish three individual elements in the buds, corresponding to the three bones in the side toes of *Merychippus*. After this, and prior to birth, the limb buds were lost. It appears that modern horses retain the genetic potential for extra toes, but that regulatory genes switch off the structural genes for side toes during embryological development. Occasionally, something goes awry with this regulatory mechanism and foals are born with side toes.[22,23,24]

Summary

The evidence of fossils, along with the study of horse embryos, indicates that the horse series is a genuine, though of course patchy, record of biological change over time. Evolutionary scientists point to this as evidence of Darwinian evolution. However, non-evolutionary scientists say that this simply records changes within the horse basic type and that there is little evidence to suggest that horses developed from a non-horse ancestor. Since the magnitude and type of change represented by the horse series can be accommodated by both evolutionary and non-evolutionary theories, it cannot therefore distinguish between them. At best, in terms of the origins debate, the horse series is neutral data.

7.7 Further Questions

1   How important is it to have a definition of "mammal" that works for fossil specimens as well as living animals?

2   Why should we be suspicious of chains of extinct animals that appear to tell a story of gradualistic evolution?

3   In which geological period do you think evolutionary biologists would like to find evidence of animals with insulating fur? What kind of future discoveries could further challenge Professor Prothero's model of mammalian evolution?

4   What kind of data could help us distinguish between the evolutionary model and the Basic Types model for variation in fossilised horses?

Chapter 7 Endnotes

1   New Scientist 1st March 2008 Page 37

2   Sidor CA (2003) *Evolutionary trends and the origin of the mammalian lower jaw* Paleobiology 29:605-40

3   Homoplasy is defined as a collection of phenomena leading to similarities in character states for reasons other than inheritance from a common ancestor. These include convergence, parallelism and reversal.

4   Kemp TS (2005) *The Origin and Evolution of Mammals* Oxford University Press page 1

5   Ibid page 2

6   Ibid page 120

7   Ibid page 122

8   Ibid page 126

9   Ibid page 133

10 Taylor DJ, Green NPO, Stout GW, Soper R (editor) (1997) *Biological Sciences 1 and 2* Cambridge University Press page 890

11 MacFadden BJ (1987) *Fossil horses from 'Eohippus' (Hyracotherium) to Equus: scaling, Cope's law, and the evolution of body size* Paleobiology 12:355-69

12 Webb SD, Hulbert RC (1986) *Systematics and evolution of Pseudhipparion (Mammalia, Equidae) from the late Neocene of the Gulf Coastal Plain and the Great Plains* in: Flanagan KM, Lillegraven JA (editors) Vertebrates, phylogeny, and philosophy. Contributions to Geology, University of Wyoming, Special Paper 3.

13 Hulbert RC (1988) *Calippus and Protohippus (Mammalia, Perissodactyla, Equidae) from the Miocene (Barstovian-early Hemphillian) of the Gulf Coastal Plain* Bulletin of the Florida State Museum of Biological Sciences 32:221-340

14 Taylor DJ, Green NPO, Stout GW, Soper R (editor) (1997) *Biological Sciences 1 and 2* Cambridge University Press

15 Roberts M, Reiss M, Monger G (2000) *Advanced Biology* Nelson Thornes

16 Scherer S (editor) (1993) *Typen des Leben*s Pascal-Verlag Berlin [German language publication]

17 Wood TC, Murray MJ (2003) *Understanding the Pattern of Life: Origins and Organization of the Species* Broadman and Holman Publishers Nashville, Tennessee

18 Cavanaugh DP, Wood TC, Wise KP (2003) *Fossil Equidae: a monobaraminic, stratomorphic series* in: Ivey RL (editor) Proceedings of the Fifth International Conference on Creationism. Creation Science Fellowship, Pittsburgh, pp.143-53

19 Garner P (1998) *It's a horse, of course! A creationist view of phylogenetic change in the equid family* Origins (25):13-23.

20 Stein-Cadenbach H (2003) *Hybriden, Chromosomenstrukturen und Artbildung bei Pferden (Equidae)* in: Scherer S (editor) Typen des Lebens. Pascal-Verlag, Berlin, pp.225-44. [German language publication]

21 Ewart JC (1894) *The development of the skeleton of the limbs of the horse, with observations on polydactyly* Journal of Anatomy and Physiology 28:342-69

22 Marsh OC (1879) *Polydactyle horses, recent and extinct.* American Journal of Science 17:499-505

23 Marsh OC (1892) *Recent polydactyle horses* American Journal of Science 43:339-55

24 Struthers J (1893) *On the development of the bones of the foot of the horse, and of digital bones generally and on a case of polydactyly in the horse* Journal of Anatomy and Physiology 28:51-62

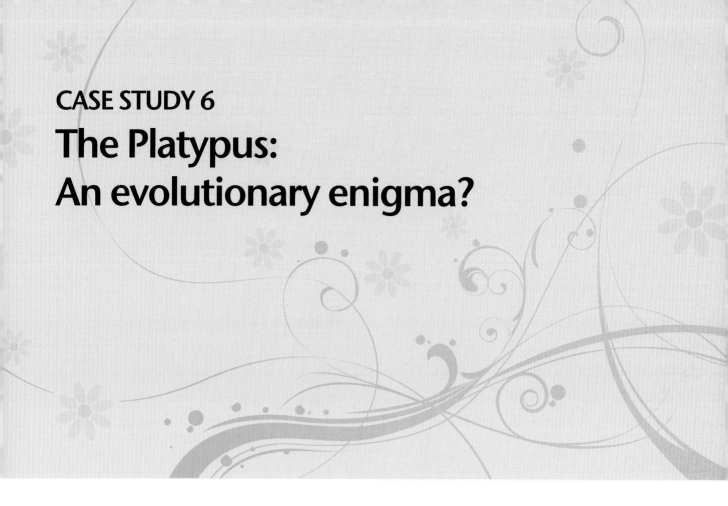

The Platypus:
An evolutionary enigma?

The platypus is an evolutionary enigma. According to Professor Tom Kemp:

> The greatest mystery of all concerning mammalian evolution stretches back for 200 years: the question of what exactly the monotreme mammals are, and how they relate phylogenetically to therians.[1]

Mammals comprise three major groups. The therians (theria) include all placental mammals (eutheria) and marsupials (metatheria), which have the characteristic pouch in which the immature foetus is nurtured after birth. The third group of mammals is the monotremes or egg-laying mammals. These are known as the prototheria and there are only three species of monotremes living today, all found in Australia. These are the platypus (*Ornithorhyncus*), the short-beaked echidna (*Tachyglossus*) and the long-beaked echidna (*Zaglossus*).

Is it a reptile?

At one time, it was believed that the monotremes were transitional between reptiles and mammals. It is easy to see why. The prototheria (from Greek, meaning "first beasts") lay small round eggs and have some other reptilian features. For example, the male platypus possesses a spur on its hind limbs through which it delivers a venomous cocktail produced by the crural glands located in its upper thigh. This venom contains hundreds of different chemicals, including four major toxins. Three of these toxins are unique to the platypus and are described as defensin-like proteins [DLPs].

Whittington *et al.* have recently published a paper in the academic journal *Genome* in which they describe significant homology (structural similarity) between the DLPs and proteins present in the venom of snakes and other reptiles.[2] However, because of the prevailing evolutionary phylogenetic classification that places reptiles and monotremes in very different clades, the general consensus is that similar venom proteins evolved independently in reptiles and monotremes. This is considered an example of convergence, in that, given appropriate conditions, similar proteins and structures can evolve multiple times, in different organisms. In their own words:

> Convergent evolution has repeatedly selected genes coding for proteins containing specific structural motifs as templates for venom molecules.

To the credit of Whittington and his colleagues, they do at least speculate on how this might have occurred by suggesting processes involving "gene duplication and subsequent functional diversification". Presumably, functional diversification must involve the repeated emergence of active protein intermediates with some selective advantage. It is interesting to ponder what these unknown proteins might have been and what particular functions they might have served. Unfortunately, this is not done here, and it very rarely is.

Nevertheless, the main reason that monotremes cannot be considered intermediate between reptiles and mammals is the current Darwinian consensus that reptiles and mammals have evolved independently from a putative common ancestral amniote, via the synapsid (leading to mammals) and the sauropsid (leading to reptiles and birds) lineages. This is explained in Chapter 7.

Consequently, it is misleading to describe the synapsids as "mammal-like reptiles", as is still commonly done in both the academic and the popular press. As mentioned in the previous chapter, Professor Prothero is dogmatic about this anomaly. In chapter 13 of his book, entitled *Mammalian Explosion*, he writes as follows:

> Of the transitional series that we have examined between major groups of vertebrates, one of the best documented is the transition from primitive amniotes to mammals via the synapsids, formerly known as the "mammal-like reptiles." As we explained previously, however, the synapsids that evolve into mammals are not reptiles and never had anything to do with the lineage that leads to reptiles... This idea is now completely discredited, and anyone who still uses the obsolete and misleading term mammal-like reptiles clearly doesn't know much about the current understanding of vertebrate evolution.[3]

Tom Kemp considers the mystery of monotreme evolution:

> The relationship of monotremes to the Mesozoic mammal groups is considerably less clear, and the development of views about this problem has had an extraordinarily chequered history. At one time it was believed by almost everyone that monotremes had a separate origin from pre-mammalian therapsids, implying convergent evolution of their mammalian characters. The discovery of late Triassic mammals of South Wales quickly altered that view because similarities were seen between, on the one hand Morganucodon and the monotremes and on the other Kuehneotherium and the living therians.[4]

As described in the preceding chapter, *Morganucodon* is generally regarded as a mammal although it also possesses some reptilian features, particularly in its lower jaw. The reason why this creature is considered a relative to the monotremes is its teeth. As Kemp points out, this is highly contentious because the platypus sheds its juvenile teeth, which are replaced in maturity by bony ridges. To complicate matters further, echidnas do not have teeth at all. The other ancient mammal referred to by Kemp, *Kuehneotherium*, has been found in exactly the same strata in South Wales (for further information see Kemp pages 162-163). After a consideration of academic attempts to relate monotremes to *Morganucodon*, Kemp concludes:

> Compared to this very weak evidence for monotreme–Morganucodon relationship, there

Figure CS6:1 The Platypus (Photo: ©)

are several characters shared by monotremes and therians that can be demonstrated to be more derived than in Morganucodon... All cladistic analyses now place monotremes closer to living therians than to morganucondontids.[5]

Since the recent publication (May 2008) of the platypus genome in the journal *Nature*[6] there has been a great deal of discussion in the academic press and in the popular media. All this activity, however, has not brought any resolution to the evolutionary enigma that is the platypus. If anything, the situation has become even more confused. For example, Elizabeth Finkel wrote a review entitled *Genome speaks to Transitional Nature of Monotremes* in the prestigious American journal *Science,* in which she states:

> The clearest traces of the journey from reptile to mammal come from tracking the yolk and milk genes. Chickens have three vitellogenin egg yolk genes; the platypus has just one left. But the casein milk protein genes that mammals have but reptiles don't are all there. And just as in other mammals, in platypus, they are clustered next to the tooth enamel genes from which they are thought to have evolved, the researchers report.[7]

Here in this statement, one can discern something of the current confusion in attempts to trace the evolutionary history of the monotremes. The suggestion here is that the platypus has, after all, evolved from a reptilian lineage (anathema to Professor Prothero!), whereas mammals, in current Darwinian thinking, have evolved from synapsids, which are not reptiles. Of course, presumably synapsids were oviparous and, like all egg-laying animals, would have possessed yolk proteins and the vitellogenin coding genes. This is a reasonable assumption since, according to Patrick Brabin in his recent paper in *Gene*[8], vitellogenin homologues have been found in amphibians, fish and birds as well as in the platypus and reptiles.

On the other hand, therian mammals (i.e. both placentals and marsupials) do not lay eggs and it might be thought that they have no need of vitellogenin genes.

In particular, David Brawand *et al.* have recently published a paper (March 18 2008) in the journal *PloS Biology*[9] entitled *Loss of Egg Yolk Genes in Mammals and the Origin of Lactation and Placentation*. In the abstract of this freely-available paper they write:

> Embryonic development in nonmammalian vertebrates depends entirely on nutritional reserves that are predominantly derived from vitellogenin proteins and stored in egg yolk. Mammals have evolved new resources, such as lactation and placentation, to nourish their developing and early offspring. However, the evolutionary timing and molecular events associated with this major phenotypic transition are not known. By means of sensitive comparative genomics analyses and evolutionary simulations, we here show that the three ancestral vitellogenin-encoding genes were progressively lost during mammalian evolution (until around 30–70 million years ago, Mya) in all but the egg-laying monotremes, which have retained a functional vitellogenin gene.

Their research identified vitellogenin pseudogenes in the previously published human and dog genomes. As described in Chapter 3, a pseudogene is essentially a non-active version of a gene – one that has been switched off. In the case of the vitellogenin genes, Brawand and his group found that there were "premature stop codons and frame-shifting insertion/deletions" in genomic regions equivalent to the active vitellogenin genes found in the chicken. Are these pseudogenes a relic of mammalian evolutionary history? Brawand and his colleagues think so, but is there another explanation?

Do placental and marsupial mammals need the ability to produce egg yolk at any stage in their life cycles? The answer is an emphatic yes! In the paradoxical words of Brawand and his group:

> Marsupials also have a placenta, originating from the yolk sac, but the marsupial oocyte [egg] contains considerably more yolk than that of eutherians, which is virtually devoid of it. The marsupial yolk reserve is assumed to be essential during the earliest development of the embryo, complementing the uptake of uterine secretions by the yolk sac, prior to shell coat rupture. However, the content of marsupial yolk is not well known.[9]

The fact is this: all mammals require yolk at some stage in development. In particular, all placental mammals produce eggs that require yolk for nourishment prior to the establishment of the placenta. In the words of LM Baggott in his book *Human Reproduction*:

> The eggs of mammals contain relatively little yolk compared to the eggs of other vertebrates. However, yolk is present in sufficient quantity to sustain the development of the embryo through the period of cleavage... In placental mammals, including of course humans; cleavage takes place as the embryo passes down the Fallopian tube towards the uterus. During this period, the embryo draws upon the reserves of yolk in the dividing cells. After implantation has taken place in the uterus and until birth, energy and raw materials come to the developing embryo from the maternal circulation.[10]

This fact might allow an alternative explanation for the presence of vitellogenin pseuodogenes in placental mammals. In fact, seen in this light, pseudogenes may sometimes be active genes that are developmentally switched off in most types of cell during cellular differentiation. For example, although a skin cell has no need of yolk, it will always possess the full genome, but with genes like the vitellogenin gene inactivated. What is much more difficult to imagine from a Darwinian perspective, however, is the stepwise emergence of a fully functional placenta with its essential corollaries. It seems impossible to comprehend the move from an oviparous (egg-laying) to a viviparous (live birth) physiology in fully-functional steps, and Brawand *et al.* do not begin to consider this, even though they include the word "placentation" in the title and abstract of their paper.

On the other hand, like all mammals,

the platypus possesses the metabolic and physiological capability to produce milk. Brawand and colleagues appear somewhat bemused by the fact that the platypus has casein (milk protein) genes. They state:

> We screened the platypus genome to see whether monotremes do in fact have orthologous casein genes, which would imply that these genes emerged in the common mammalian ancestor. Interestingly, we identified three putative casein genes in a genomic region that is syntenic to that carrying the casein genes in therians.[8]

Two genes are said to be orthologous (a Darwinian term) if they diverged after a speciation event. For genomic regions to be 'syntenic' they must be located on the same or orthologous chromosomes. The language of the Brawand paper is remarkable: "we identified three putative casein genes in a genomic region that is syntenic to that carrying the casein genes in therians" – apparently they expected to find them in a totally different location because they are supposed to be a case of convergent evolution. But the fact is that all mammalian lactation requires that all the genes for the production of all the protein constituents of milk are present, and that the physical structures necessary to deliver that milk are functional. In a design model, their co-location on the same chromosome is not surprising.

The platypus, however, does not suckle its young in the conventional mammalian manner. It does not have nipples but exudes milk from specialised glands on its abdomen. These glands are generally regarded as modified sweat glands. For example, Lewis Wolpert wrote:

> One important piece of evidence is the platypus, a monotreme mammal that has a patch on its breast that secretes milk for its infants to suck... Clearly; the platypus was an early stage in breast evolution. Numerous theories have been proposed for how lactation evolved in the platypus. One theory, more than a hundred years old, suggests that the glands secreting nourishment in the platypus are modified sweat glands, but that the lactating glands in other mammals are modified sebaceous glands, which normally secrete an oily fluid to protect the skin. In the 1960s, JBS Haldane took up the problem and proposed that the ancestors of monotreme mammals might have needed to keep their eggs cool, and so evolved a mechanism for moistening them in their fur, in a manner similar to that used by some Asian birds who moisten their feathers. More recently a theory has emerged in which multiple glands of the skin are involved.[11]

According to Professor Wolpert and others, lactation in the platypus was an "early stage in breast evolution" perhaps being required to keep eggs cool by secreting milk from modified sweat glands. Let us evaluate this hypothesis objectively.

Sweat glands are characteristic of warm-blooded mammals; reptiles and birds do not possess sweat glands. Now, mammalian skin has two types of sweat glands: apocrine and merocrine. The secretion from both these types is controlled by the endocrine and the autonomic nervous systems. Apocrine sweat glands produce a thick secretion containing pheromones. Merocrine sweat glands are more widely distributed and are closely involved in temperature regulation and excretion by secreting sweat, which is 99% water.

So we have two problems:

1. For the lactation machinery to evolve from a sweat gland there has to be a functioning sweat gland, yet reptiles do not possess sweat glands. There is no requirement for sweat glands until the animal has evolved an endothermic physiology. In other words, a mammal has to be a mammal to possess a sweat gland.
2. Since sweat is 99% water, why would all the milk protein coding genes evolve just to keep the eggs cool? Of course, milk has no nutritional benefit for a developing embryo encased in a monotreme egg.

If, as Professor Wolpert and others suggest, lactation in the platypus is the beginning of the evolution of the breast (presumably the nipple and the machinery associated with it), one has to assume that all the ancient mammals from the mid-Triassic to the Cretaceous had monotreme-like oviparous physiology, even though there is no fossil evidence to suggest that this is true. The general Darwinian consensus (also reflected in the *Nature* paper on the platypus genome) is that the monotremes diverged from the other mammals approximately 166 million years ago.

Nevertheless, the oldest known fossils recognisable as monotremes, including *Teinolophos trusleri*, *Steropodon galmani* and *Kollikodon ritchiei*, are conventionally dated at approximately 100 to 120 million years ago. This is supposedly 100 million years after the emergence of true mammals in the fossil record in the late Triassic.

The situation is made even more confusing by the discovery of several mammalian fossils in the southern hemisphere that possess tribosphenic (three-cusped) molars. These teeth are characteristic of all marsupials and placental mammals, which were thought to have emerged initially only in the northern hemisphere. For example, Thomas Rich of the Museum of Victoria in Melbourne spent many years looking for the ancestors of Australia's mammals. In the late 1990s he discovered an ancient jaw which he and his co-workers subsequently described in a publication in the journal *Science*. In the abstract we read:

> A small, well-preserved dentary of a tribosphenic mammal with the most posterior premolar and all three molars in place has been found in Aptian (Early Cretaceous) rocks of south-eastern Australia. In most respects, dental and mandibular anatomy of the specimen is similar to that of primitive placental mammals.[12]

Rich called this animal *Austribosphenos nyktos* and since that time several other fossils have been found in Australia (*Bishops*),

Madagascar (*Ambondro mahabo*) and South America (*Asfaltomylos*) that seem to indicate an emergence of placental animals in the fossil record that predates the most ancient monotremes. This has been extremely controversial. For example, Luo *et al.* proposed independent convergent evolution for tribosphenic teeth in the northern and southern hemispheres.[13] The most extensive cladistic analysis of mammalian fossil dental characteristics that has been undertaken was published in 2003 in the journal *Molecular Phylogenetics and Evolution*.[14] In the words of Kemp:

> Woodburne et al. (2003) undertook a cladistic analysis, based on 51 characters, mostly dental but a few mandibular. They found that monotremes, including Steropodon and Teinolophos as basal members, are a sister group of all the therian mammals. Furthermore the disputed genera Ambondro, Ausktribophenos, Asfaltomylos, and Bishops constituted a monophyletic group that nests within the stem placentals.[15]

More recently, another 'mammal-like' fossil has been discovered in mid-Jurassic sediments in Mongolia which may eventually lead to a total revision of Darwinian understanding of the emergence of mammals. The creature has been called *Castorocauda lutrasimilis*.

This discovery was first described by Ji *et al.* in a 2006 paper entitled *A Swimming Mammaliaform from the Middle Jurassic and Ecomorphological Diversification of Early Mammals* in the journal *Science*.[16] They conclude their descriptive paper as follows:

> *Castorocauda* was a semiaquatic carnivore, similar to the modern river otter. This fossil shows that basal mammals occupied more diverse niches than just those of small insectivorous or omnivorous mammals with generalized terrestrial locomotory features. *Castorocauda* also suggests that mammaliaforms developed physiological adaptations associated with pelage [fur], well before the rise of modern Mammalia, and had

more diverse ecomorphological adaptations than previously thought, with at least some lineages occupying semiaquatic niches.

At the present time, *Castorocauda* is not regarded as a true mammal. According to current Darwinian thinking, the creature can only be regarded as a mammaliaform or proto-mammal. Nevertheless, the most remarkable feature of this fossil discovery is the preservation of its fur. According to Ji *et al.*:

> The fur of *Castorocauda* is preserved as impressions of guard hairs and carbonized under-furs. Hairs and hair-related integument structures are important characteristics of all modern mammals ... the broad and scaly tail of *Castorocauda* was similar to that of the modern beaver *Castor canadensis*, a semiaquatic placental mammal well adapted for swimming.

The presence of fur is a clear indication that the animal was warm-blooded and although the animal appears most like a semi-aquatic placental mammal (e.g. beaver or otter), the authors suggest that the forelimbs are similar to the platypus in that they are adapted for both digging and swimming. There is also an indication of webbing on the hind feet. Furthermore, according to the *National Geographic*:

> Even tiny middle-ear bones are intact. The well-preserved teeth - incisors, canines, premolars, and molars - look to have been ideal for feeding on fish and aquatic invertebrates, somewhat like the teeth of modern seals... *Castorocauda* has the ankle spurs characteristic of its nearest living relative, the platypus, which uses them for territorial defense. And like the platypus, *Castorocauda* was probably an egg-layer.[17]

So was *Castorocauda* an ancient monotreme? According to Kemp, "the solution to the mystery of the monotremes continues to be elusive". Presumably, this will remain the situation until there is some major revision in current Darwinian thinking.

Is it a bird?

Perhaps the most remarkable feature of the platypus genome is the structure and number of sex chromosomes. Typically, all male mammals have one X and one Y chromosome (they are heterogametic) whereas females possess two X chromosomes (they are homogametic). The male platypus has five X and five Y chromosomes and the female platypus five pairs of X chromosomes. In most mammals, the Y chromosome possesses a gene called SRY which is a major sex determining factor but this appears to be absent in the platypus. In addition, there also appears to be no homology between the X chromosomes of placental mammals and the platypus. Sex determination in the platypus is therefore something of a mystery and a great deal of research is continuing in order to discover its mechanism.

Several groups have reported the identification of a gene called DMRT1 on the X5 chromosome of the platypus. DMRT1 is thought to be a sex determining factor in birds! The avian sex chromosomes are called Z and W (as distinct from X and Y), and, unlike mammals, male birds are homogametic (ZZ), while females are heterogametic (ZW). DMRT1 is found on the Z chromosome of birds, and the double dose of DMRT1 in male birds is thought to be a trigger for sex determination. Elizabeth Finkel suggests:

> The story of the platypus' march away from the reptilian world is also told in the sex chromosomes. According to Jenny Graves of the Australian National University in Canberra, sex chromosome wise, "they do it like a chicken"... The genome sequence now shows that one of the platypus X chromosomes [X5] has more than just that one bird gene: It's almost entirely equivalent to the chicken Z chromosome.[6]

More recent evidence supporting the contention that sex determination in the platypus is similar to that in birds has recently been published in *Genome Research*. In the abstract to their paper, Veyrunes *et al.* state:

> Most significantly, comparative mapping shows that, contrary to earlier reports, there is no homology between the platypus and therian X chromosomes. Orthologs of genes in the conserved region of the human X (including SOX3, the gene from which SRY evolved) all map to platypus chromosome 6, which therefore represents the ancestral autosome from which the therian X and Y pair derived. Rather, the platypus X chromosomes have substantial homology with the bird Z chromosome (including DMRT1) and to segments syntenic with this region in the human genome. Thus, platypus sex chromosomes have strong homology with bird, but not to therian sex chromosomes, implying that the therian X and Y chromosomes (and the SRY gene) evolved from an autosomal pair after the divergence of monotremes only 166 million years ago. Therefore, the therian X and Y are more than 145 million years younger than previously thought.[18]

So do the platypus and the other monotremes share any common ancestry with birds? According to the current Darwinian hypothesis, birds are viewed as living dinosaurs, in that they are thought to have descended from sauropsid ancestors. As mentioned in Chapter 7, the sauropsids are distinct from the synapsids, the supposed ancestors of the mammalian line. However, this model has become even more unworkable with the recent suggestion that there are multiple independent origins for sex determination in amniotes.[19] In the review of this work, Vallender and Lahn suggest:

> It is generally accepted that environmental sex determination is the ancestral state and that genetic sex determination evolved as a derived condition. It is also recognized that genetic sex determination is evolutionarily highly labile, having evolved into existence *on many independent occasions across diverse taxa* [emphasis added]. A case in point is sex-determination mechanisms in amniotes (a clade encompassing reptiles, birds, and mammals). The ancestral state in amniotes is likely temperature-dependent sex determination, which is still found in many extant reptilian species, such as crocodilians and some turtles and lizards. From this ancestral state, genetic sex determination evolved in birds, which utilize the ZZ:ZW system, and also independently in mammals, which use the XX:XY system.[20]

This problem has been discussed in detail with particular reference to the platypus in the most recent review by Wallis *et al.*, published in the journal *Cellular and Molecular Life Sciences* in 2008. They conclude their review as follows:

> Interest in elucidating the sex-determining system from which SRY assumed control in therians has intensified following our recent finding that the sex chromosomes of birds and monotremes share homology. The possibility that the ancestor of amniotes harboured a sex chromosome system still maintained in monotremes and birds today, while intriguing, still faces several obstacles: the apparent lack of homology between many amniote sex chromosomes, the frequency of subsequent transitions to temperature sex determination in reptiles, and the inferred sex heterogamety transition using the same sex chromosomes.[21]

In these last two quotes; we can appreciate something of the Darwinian dilemma. Vallender and Lahn suggest that "the ancestral state in amniotes is likely temperature-dependent sex determination" whereas Wallis *et al.* are tempted to conclude "that the ancestor of amniotes harboured a sex chromosome system still maintained in monotremes and birds today". The sex chromosome system in monotremes (indeed all mammals) and birds does not involve temperature-dependent sex determination. As we have seen, sex determination systems in reptiles, birds, monotremes and the therian mammals (both marsupial and placental) are all very different and distinctive. Furthermore, with these independent, multiple and, in some cases, convergent evolutionary events supposedly taking place, the maintenance of fertility is of paramount importance.

Of course, there are also other genetic features that appear to be unique to the platypus. These include the possession of all the biology required for the exquisitely sensitive chemical and electrical detection systems in its leathery bill. In particular, researchers have discovered numerous genes coding for odour (vomeronasal) receptors. Similar genes are found in many other mammals that rely on a sense of smell, the dog being a classic example. The platypus, however, requires this sensitivity underwater. In 2007, Wendy Grus and her colleagues at the University of Michigan published a major article on these odour receptors in the platypus.[22] In addition, John Pettigrew of the University of Queensland has written an important review entitled *Electroreception in monotremes* in the *Journal of Experimental Biology*. According to Pettigrew:

> Its complexity belies the common misconception that monotremes are in some way primitive. The close apposition of mechanoreception and electroreception systems in platypus cortex raises new questions about their relationship.[23]

In other words, the brain of the monotreme is specifically wired to give the creature its remarkable abilities. It is not at all surprising, therefore, following the publication of the platypus genome, that this uniqueness is reflected in the genes of this amazing creature. In fact, whatever the platypus does, it will require the genes to enable it to do so. It is like a bird as it lays eggs. It is like a reptile as it produces venom. It is a warm–blooded, fur-covered mammal producing milk to suckle its young. It has a unique electro-sensory system and can detect odours and pheromones underwater with unparalleled sensitivity. It is worth noting that the other main group of vertebrates that rely on electroreception is fish and sharks.

Thus the platypus will probably remain a significant misfit in any Darwinian scheme. Is it from a sauropsid lineage which includes reptiles and birds? Is it from a synapsid lineage which supposedly led to the emergence of the mammals? Is it derived independently from some unknown ancestral amniote? Or could it be that the Darwinian model, based on cladistic analysis, is just far too restrictive? Without doubt, there are mammal-like reptiles as there are reptile-like mammals. The platypus is a Darwinian cautionary tale. Is it a bird or is it a plain... old platypus?

Further Questions

1   How does the platypus challenge any theory for the emergence of mammals?

2   Does the platypus demonstrate the limitations of any system of classification?

Case Study 6 Endnotes

1   Kemp TS (2007) *The Origin and Evolution of Mammals* Oxford University Press pp. 173-4

2   http://genome.cshlp.org/content/18/6/986.full

3   Prothero DR (2007) *Evolution: What the Fossils Say and Why It Matters* New York Columbia University Press p.271

4   Kemp TS (2007) *The Origin and Evolution of Mammals* Oxford University Press p.175

5   Ibid page 176

6   http://www.nature.com/nature/journal/v453/n7192/full/nature06936.html

7   Finkel E (2008) *Genome Speaks to Transitional Nature of Monotremes* Science 320:730

8   Babin PT (2008) *Conservation of a vitellogenin gene cluster in oviparous vertebrates and identification of its traces in the platypus genome* Gene 413:76-82

9   Brawand D, Wahli W, Kaessmann H (2008) *Loss of Egg Yolk Genes in Mammals and the Origin of Lactation and Placentation* PLoS Biol 6: e63. http://www.plosbiology.org/article/info:doi/10.1371/journal.pbio.0060063

10   Baggott LM (1997) *Human Reproduction* Cambridge University Press p.33

11   *The Independent* [December 8 2004]

12   Rich TH *et al.* (1997) *A Tribosphenic Mammal from the Mesozoic of Australia* Science 278:1438-42

13   Zhe-Xi Luo *et al.* (2001) *Dual origin of tribosphenic mammals* Nature 409:53-7

14   Woodburn MO *et al.* (2003) *The evolution of tribosphery and the antiquity of mammalian clades* Mol Phylogenet Evol 28:360-85

15   Kemp TS (2007) *The Origin and Evolution of Mammals* Oxford University Press p.180

16   Ji *et al. A Swimming Mammaliaform from the Middle Jurassic and Ecomorphological Diversification of Early Mammals* Science 24 February 2006:1123-7

17   http://news.nationalgeographic.com/news/2006/02/0223_060223_beaver.html

18   http://genome.cshlp.org/content/18/6/965.long

19   Matsubara K *et al.* (2006) *Evidence for different origin of sex chromosomes in snakes, birds, and mammals and step-wise differentiation of snake sex chromosomes* PNAS 103:18190-5

20   http://www.pnas.org/content/103/48/18031.full

21   Wallis MC *et al.* (2008) *Sex determination in mammals--before and after the evolution of SRY* Cell Mol Life Sci 65:3182-95

22   http://mbe.oxfordjournals.org/content/24/10/2153.full.pdf+html

23   http://jeb.biologists.org/cgi/reprint/202/10/1447.pdf

Chapter 8
Man from Apes?

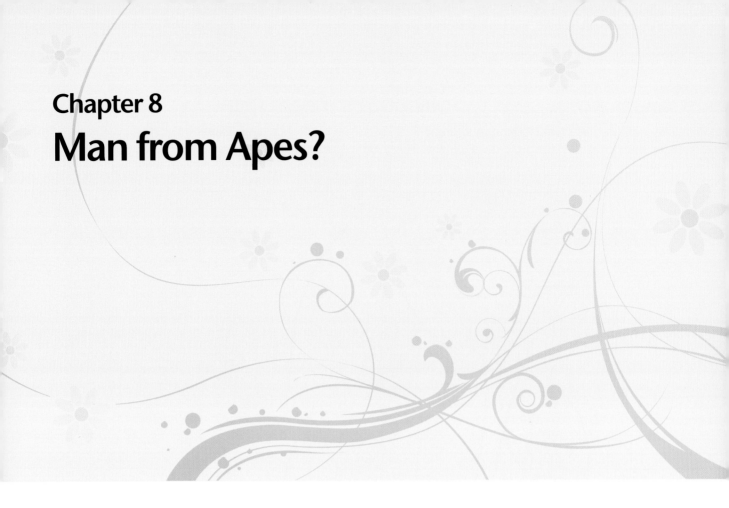

8.1 Introduction

There are very striking differences between chimps and humans that any evolutionary model must consider in order to have a workable scheme of primate ancestry for humans. Up until the 1980s, paleoanthropologists classified ancient human and ape fossil remains collectively as hominoids, which was subdivided into the subfamilies hominids (humans and their ancestors) and anthropoids (chimps, gorillas, and orangutans). However, it is now generally assumed that humans are more closely related to chimps and gorillas than to orangutans. Accordingly, hominoids now comprise two different subfamilies, namely, Ponginae (orangutans) and Homininae (humans and their ancestors, and chimps and gorillas). Homininae have been further subdivided into Hominini [sic] (humans and their ancestors), Panini (chimps), and Gorillini (gorillas).

Thus a hominin is defined as a human or a human ancestor. These include all of the *Homo* species (*Homo sapiens, H. erectus* etc.) and all the Australopithecines as well as other species such as *Paranthropus* and *Ardipithecus*. An overview of human evolution is shown in Figure 8.1.

8.2 Sahelanthropus Tchadensis

Sahelanthropus tchadensis was discovered by a team led by Michel Brunet of the University of Poitiers, France[1] and has been suggested as the most ancient of any fossil hominin, having a conventional date of approximately 7 million years (see Figure 8.1). However, a team led by Milford Wolpoff and including Brigitte Senut and Martin Pickford, the discoverers of *Orrorin tugenensis*, have suggested that the features of *Sahelanthropus tchadensis* are more characteristic of a female proto-gorilla.[2] A comparison of the skulls of each of these

Millions of Years Ago

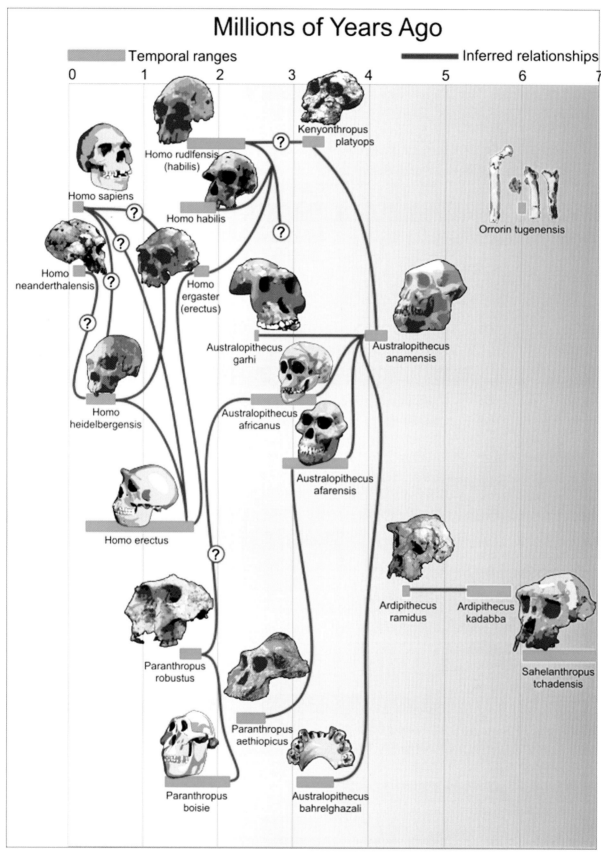

Temporal ranges — Inferred relationships

0   1   2   3   4   5   6   7

Kenyonthropus platyops

Homo rudlfensis (habilis)

Homo sapiens

Homo habilis

Orrorin tugenensis

Homo neanderthalensis

Homo ergaster (erectus)

Australopithecus anamensis

Australopithecus garhi

Homo heidelbergensis

Australopithecus africanus

Australopithecus afarensis

Homo erectus

Ardipithecus ramidus

Ardipithecus kadabba

Paranthropus robustus

Sahelanthropus tchadensis

Paranthropus aethiopicus

Paranthropus boisie

Australopithecus bahrelghazali

Figure 8.1 Human evolution according to conventional evolutionary thinking

can be seen in Figure 8.2.

The main problem is the reconstruction of the ancient skull, which had been badly crushed. There are two main features that encourage the assignment of any given fossil to the hominid lineage. These are dental anatomy (particularly the presence or absence of pronounced canine teeth) and the position of the foramen magnum, one of the several apertures in the base of the skull through which the spinal cord enters. The specific location of the foramen magnum can give some indication regarding uprightness of stance and the likelihood of bipedal locomotion. Nevertheless, there is significant variability in the position of the foramen magnum even in living apes.[3]

Although there is a serious conflict of interest, it appears that Wolpoff, Senut and Pickford may be right in arguing that *Sahelanthropus tchadensis* may well be an ancient gorilla. However, to be consistent with the prevailing paradigm, the creature has to be

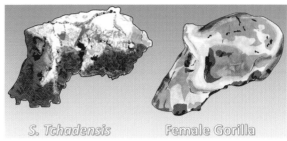
Figure 8.2 A comparison of skulls (1)

regarded as a *proto*-gorilla. The reason for this is the date assigned to the fossil. Apparently, there were no gorillas seven million years ago.

However, it has been difficult to assign an exact age to the fossil as it was discovered partially exposed in loose sand. It has been suggested that this sediment might not be the material the bones were originally deposited in. Indirect methods of dating are generally used in this situation. For example, other fauna found in similar sediments are often employed to give an indication of age, and assumptions have to be made that cannot be corroborated. Thus the "oldest known hominin" is a very tenuous case.

8.3 Orrorin Tugenensis

Fragments of *Orrorin tugenensis* (see Figure 8.3) were discovered by the team of Brigit Senut[4] and is currently considered the second-oldest known hominin, as well as the only species classified in the genus *Orrorin*. The name was given for the fact that the fossil was discovered in the Tugen Hills of Kenya. The strata in which it was found have been dated between 6.1 and 5.8 million years ago.

As previously indicated, dating fossils is not a trivial problem, since the age of the strata may or may not reflect the age of the fossil. In particular, the radiometric date of the strata must normally be older than the fossil. This is because the process of fossilisation normally involves rapid and complete inundation with pre-existing sediments and, these sediments have been produced by the erosion of pre-existing igneous rock. Therefore radiometric procedures are of little use to date the time when fossilisation occurred. In many

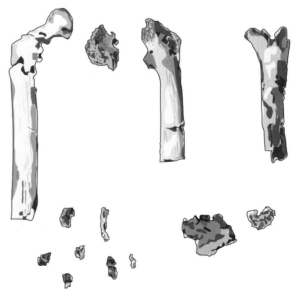
Figure 8.3 Fragments of Orrorin tugenensis

instances, the presumed age of other fossil fauna present in the same (or similar) strata has to be used to identify an approximate age of any particular fossil. This methodology is termed biostratigraphic correlation[5], and assumes that all the other fossil remains were deposited at approximately the same time and that some of them can be reliably dated – which is normally done by reference to their presumed stage in an evolutionary sequence.

According to the scientists who found them, the *Orrorin* fossils are from at least five different individuals. Furthermore, there is no way of knowing whether each of these individuals is actually from the same species. Indeed, different conclusions are reached from considering each individual item. For

example, the neck of the fossil femur gives some indication that the creature walked on two legs (was bipedal). Other parts seem very chimpanzee-like. The discoverers concluded that *Orrorin* is a hominin on the basis of its bipedal locomotion and dental anatomy. Interestingly, they used this argument to date the specimens, as the current dogma suggests that the evolutionary split between hominins and African great apes was at least 7 million years ago. However, this date is different from those derived using other dating methods. It is worth taking time to reflect on this fact.

8.4 Ardipithecus

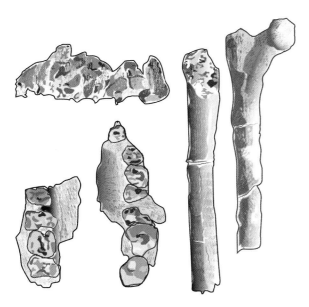

Figure 8.4 Fragments of Ardipithecus ramidus

Similarly to *Orrorin*, the discovery of *Ardipithecus* generated a great deal of excitement and media attention.[6] It is

considered to be an early hominin, dated by a variety of methods at 4.4 million years ago during the early Pliocene.[7] Nevertheless, because *Ardipithecus* has very similar characteristics to the African great apes, it is considered by some to be an ancient chimpanzee rather than a human ancestor. Others disagree because it has teeth that are very similar to *Australopithecus*. Some of the fossil fragments are illustrated in Figure 8.4.

Ardipithecus ramidus was found in September 1994. It was dated at 4.4 million years ago because it was located between two volcanic strata which could be dated using traditional radiometric technology. Subsequent finds have been dated even older, at 5.8 million years ago. Again, fossils have been found from many different individuals over a very wide area (in the Afar Depression in the Middle Awash river valley of Ethiopia).

8.5 Australopithecus Afarensis

Perhaps the most famous of all putative hominins is *Australopithecus afarensis* which has been dated between 3.9 and 2.9 million years. Fossils have been found exclusively in eastern Africa. In particular, most fossils assigned to this species have been discovered in Hadar, Ethiopia.

In November 1973, the anthropologist Donald Johanson discovered a fossil of a

proximal tibia, the upper end of a shinbone. Originally he thought it was from a monkey until he found a distal femur, the lower end of a thighbone in close proximity. The two fossils fitted together with other fragments to form a distinct knee joint from a creature that was bipedal.[8] The following year (1974), Johanson and his team, searching in a gully about two and a half kilometres from the site where the knee joint had been discovered, found the first fossil fragments of a creature they called "Lucy". Her partial skeleton is shown in Figure 8.5.

There is no way of knowing if all the fragments of Lucy's skeleton actually come from a single individual or even species. For example, the hip bones and femur of Lucy are very human-like. Milford Wolpoff of the University of Michigan has argued that Lucy's small legs are the length one would expect in a human of her diminutive stature.[9] On the other hand, other skulls assigned to this species have many characteristics in common with chimpanzees. This is shown in Figure 8.6.

The most appreciable difference in the two skulls shown in Figure 8.6 is the dentition, with much more pronounced canine teeth in the modern chimpanzee. The other notable feature suggested for *Australopithecus afarensis* is the ability to walk upright.

8.6 Bipedalism

Bipedalism brings many advantages, such as greater vision and freedom for the hands to use tools and carry food. From the partial skeleton of Lucy, it is usually concluded that *Australopithecus afarensis* was almost exclusively bipedal. Others have considered the anatomy of the hands, feet and shoulder joints and suggested more of a tree-dwelling habit. In particular, the curvature of the finger and toe bones is very similar to modern-day apes and reflects their ability to grasp branches and climb. The problem for Lucy is that no remains of hands and feet have been assigned to her skeleton.

Incidentally, this may be a further indication that the species *Australopithecus afarensis* is a compilation of several different species, some ape and some hominin. Of course, dating these fossils at 3.75 million years ago prevents their being assigned to *Homo sapiens* in the conventional evolutionary framework.

Many investigators have concluded that the sacrum and pelvis region of Lucy (AL

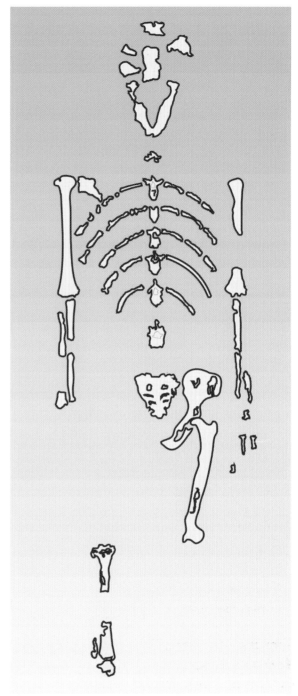

Figure 8.5 Lucy's Remains

288-1) are very human-like and imply a bipedal gait (see Figure 8.5 and the writings of Lewin [1999] for example). The iliac blades of the partial hip remains are short and wide.[10] Similarly, the sacrum is wide and positioned directly behind the hip joint. This is illustrated in Figure 8.7. All these facts suggest the pelvis may be of a hominin. Not all share this view. Stern and Sussman state:

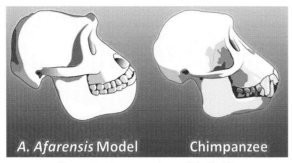

Figure 8.6 A comparison of skulls (2)

The fact that the anterior portion of the iliac blade faces laterally in humans but not in chimpanzees is obvious. The marked resemblance of AL 288-1 (Lucy) to the chimpanzee is equally obvious. It suggests to us that the mechanism of lateral pelvic balance during bipedalism was closer to that in apes than in humans.[11]

However, Lovejoy, who did further investigations, came to the conclusion that the pelvis had suffered damage in fossilisation[12] and argued that "…while much of the iliac blade is well preserved, the posterior third has been crushed, crumpled, and bent anterolaterally almost exactly 90 degrees". Accordingly, many have accepted the argument that the crushed pelvis gives it an ape-like look, but that really it was hominoid, and that Lucy was

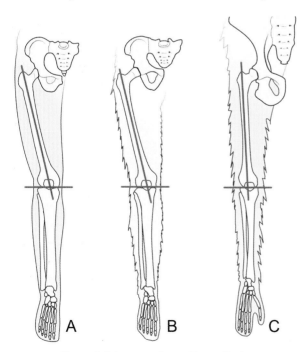

Figure 8.7 A comparison of lower limbs
A. Human B. Lucy C. Ape (1)[13]

thus bipedal.

Against this, it is important to note that an article in *Science News* (April 8, 2000, p. 235, based on a study by Richmond and Strait in *Nature*) reported that: "*A. anamemsis* and *A. afarensis* – the latter represented by the famous skeleton known as Lucy – had wrists capable of locking the hands in place during knuckle walking." This would be inconsistent with a bipedal gait. We see that it is debatable whether Lucy walked on two limbs or four, but no-one has suggested she was equally at ease doing both.

Obstacles to Bipedalism

Various characteristics are necessary for a creature to walk on two legs, and any creature which was in transition from the chimp-like posture to the human-like one would be highly unstable in walking. This is because in chimps the weight of the body is forward and the centre of gravity does not lie above the pelvic girdle – the animal does not have a stable totally upright position. However in humans, the centre of gravity when in the upright position is right over the pelvic area (see Figure 8.8) and a locking knee joint (see next section) is important. Any in-between state would be unstable and a great disadvantage for such a hypothetical creature.

As a result of bipedal locomotion, the weight of the body is transmitted to the

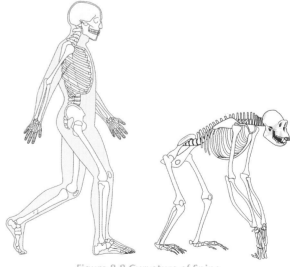

Figure 8.8 Curvature of Spine

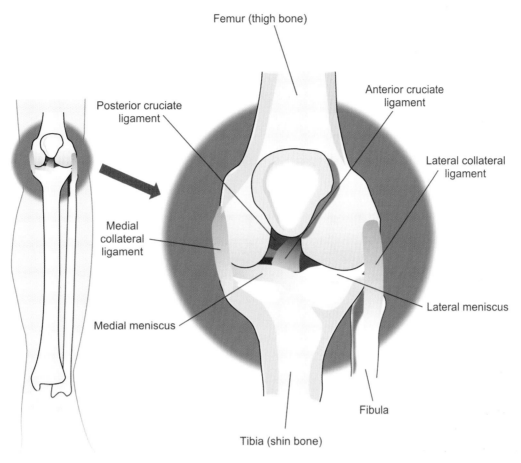

Femur (thigh bone)

Anterior cruciate ligament

Posterior cruciate ligament

Lateral collateral ligament

Medial collateral ligament

Lateral meniscus

Medial meniscus

Fibula

Tibia (shin bone)

Figure 8.9 The Human Knee Joint

lower limb via the pelvis. This allows several specialisations in the architecture of the skeleton, joints and muscles of the lower limb.[14]

According to Stuart Burgess (Professor of Engineering Design at Bristol University), the knee joint is the largest and most complex joint in the human body (see Figure 8.9).[15] The human knee joint is unique in that it can be locked in an upright position. According to Burgess:

> The knee joint is an irreducible joint because each of its four complex parts needs to exist simultaneously and in a complex assembly to be able to perform its basic function. The two bones are essential because they perform the rolling and sliding motion. The two cruciate ligaments are essential because they act as mechanical linkages and perform a vital guiding function in the joint… If just one ligament is removed, then the joint cannot function as a hinge, and

the joint can have no useful function.

In the case of monkeys and apes, the knee cannot be straightened and must be continually loaded in flexion (bent leg). It is extremely difficult for monkeys and apes to maintain a vertical posture with their legs.

The arm bones (ulna, radius, and humerus) in the human are approximately 70% of the size of its leg bones (femur, fibula, tibia). This is very different from the ape. Apes that swing (like the gibbons) have arm bones 120% larger than their leg bones and apes that knuckle-walk have arm bones about the same size as their leg bones. Since apes are knuckle-walkers, their shoulder bones (scapulas) are pointed down towards the ground. A human's scapula sits right on the back. The curvature of the spine is "S" shaped in humans, unlike in apes. Some of these characteristics have been shown in Figure 8.8.

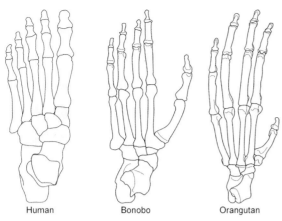

Human   Bonobo   Orangutan

Figure 8.10 A comparison of human and ape feet

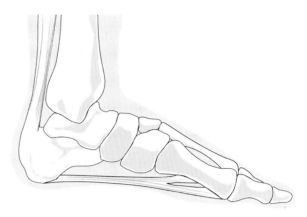

Figure 8.11 The Human Foot Platform

Finally, the human foot is quite distinct from that of an ape. According to Wang and Crompton:

> The results show… that the presence of an high arch in the human foot reduces forces in the musculature and has a lower total of force in joints and muscles than do the ape feet. These results indicate that the proportions of the human

foot and the height of the medial arch are indeed better optimized for bipedal standing than those of apes.[16]

A comparison of human and ape feet is shown in Figures 8.10 and 8.11. It can be seen that the great toe is enlarged and in line with the other toes.

8.7 The Laetoli Footprints

In 1978, Mary Leakey and her team discovered a trail of what appeared to be human footprints at Laetoli, 30 miles south of the Olduvai Gorge. However, when the radiometric date of strata above the footprints was calculated, the date of 3.8 million years ruled out the possibility of human origin because of the prevailing paradigm. The footprints comprise three parallel trails, made by three individuals, with one individual walking in the footprints of another. The trails consist of 69 prints extending about 30 yards and were made in fresh volcanic ash spewed out of Mount Sadiman to the east. There is a general consensus that the Laetoli footprints are very human-like. On the other hand, fossil foot bones generally assigned to *Australopithecus afarensis* are very ape-like.

Russell Tuttle of the University of Chicago has suggested that the feet nominally assigned to *A.afarensis* are totally incompatible with the Laetoli prints, which he believes were made by habitually unshod individuals. As

an example, Tuttle studied the Machiguenga Indians in the rugged mountains of Peru and concluded:

> In discernible features, the Laetoli G prints are indistinguishable from those of habitually barefoot Homo sapiens… Casts of Laetoli G-1 and of the Machiguenga footprints in moist, sandy soil further illustrate the remarkable humanness of Laetoli hominid feet in all detectable morphological features.[17]

In an article in the March 1990 issue of *Natural History*, Tuttle confessed that "we are left with somewhat of a mystery."[18] He also suggested in the same article:

> If the G footprints were not known to be so old, we would readily conclude that they were made by a member of our genus, Homo.

Very recently, David Raichlen *et al.* published a paper entitled *Laetoli Footprints*

Preserve Earliest Direct Evidence of Human-Like Bipedal Biomechanics. They confirmed that the Laetoli hominins walked with weight transfer most similar to the economical extended limb bipedalism of humans.[19] They state:

> These results provide us with the earliest direct

evidence of kinematically human-like bipedalism currently known, and show that extended limb bipedalism evolved long before the appearance of the genus Homo. Since extended-limb bipedalism is more energetically economical than ape-like bipedalism, energy expenditure was likely an important selection pressure on hominin bipeds by 3.6 Ma.

8.8 Australopithecus Africanus

This name is used for a species of which the first fossils were found in South Africa. Dr Raymond Dart, Professor of Anatomy at Witwatersrand University in Johannesburg, was the first to study these fossils. In 1924 at Taung in South Africa, Dart discovered a fossil skull consisting of a full face, teeth and jaws, and an endocranial cast of the brain.[20] The brain size was 410cc. Its age is currently believed to be around two to three million years old. Dart was convinced that some teeth were human-like and thus he concluded it was transitional between apes and humans. His opinions on the matter of this particular skull

were largely scorned by the scientists of this time who considered it nothing more than a young chimpanzee or gibbon. A comparison of skulls is shown in Figure 8.12.

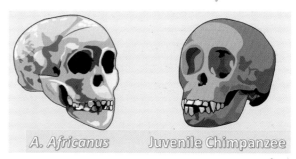

Figure 8.12 Comparison of Skulls (3)

8.9 Lucy's Child – a Case of Déjà vu?

In 2006, the journal *Nature* reported the find of a skull and partial skeleton that were recovered by Zeresenay Alemseged and his team at Dikika, Ethiopia.[21] The find was given the name *Selam* and has become known as "Lucy's child", having been assigned to the species *Australopithecus afarensis*. The material was discovered over a period of the 2000, 2002 and 2003 field seasons, and the delay in publication was due to the need to remove the main fossil from the block of sandstone sediment in which it was encased.

As with other collections of fossil material, there is no way of being certain that all the material comes from one individual. In the words of the authors of the *Nature* publication:

> The find includes many previously unknown skeletal elements from the Pliocene hominin

record, including a hyoid bone that has typical African ape morphology. The foot and other evidence from the lower limb provide clear evidence for bipedal locomotion, but the gorilla-like scapula and long and curved manual phalanges raise new questions about the importance of arboreal behaviour in the A. afarensis locomotor repertoire.

All of this material was collected over a three-year period by different researchers. The scapula, found with some ribs, is almost certainly from a gorilla, as Figure 8.13 indicates.

Nevertheless, the most remarkable characteristic of *Selam* is the skull itself. It has an appearance remarkably similar to the skull found by Raymond Dart which was assigned to *Australopithecus africanus*. This

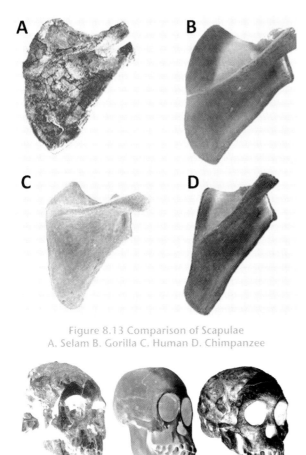

Figure 8.13 Comparison of Scapulae
A. Selam B. Gorilla C. Human D. Chimpanzee

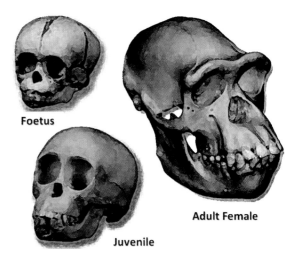

Foetus

Adult Female

Juvenile

Figure 8.15 Comparison of Skulls (5)

Selam
A. Afarensis

Juvenile
Chimpanzee

Taung Child
A. Africanus

Figure 8.14 Comparison of Skulls (4)

Figure 8.16 Chimpanzee Posture in Baby and Adult[26]

is admitted by the authors of the paper in *Nature*:

> Size and proportions of the DIK-1-1 face resemble those of the juvenile specimens A.L. 333-105 and Taung, assigned to A. afarensis and A. africanus, respectively.

Seeing pictures of Zeresenay Alemseged with *Selam*[22] brings back memories of photographs taken in the 1920s of Raymond Dart holding the skull of the Taung child in his hands[23], a definite case of déjà vu. The similarity of the skulls is illustrated in Figure 8.14.

These close similarities suggest that the classification of specimens into *afarensis* and *africanus* is somewhat speculative. Nevertheless, the fact that the skull of *Selam* is from a young ape is confirmed by the remarkable preservation of the hyoid bone.[24]

The current position of the hyoid bone beneath the palate precludes a comprehensive analysis of its morphology, but some diagnostic features can be observed and measured. It is most similar to that of juvenile African apes, and unlike that of modern humans… Its similarities with *Pan* and *Gorilla* hyoids suggest that the bulla-shaped body is the primitive condition for African apes and humans, rather than the more shallow, bar-like body shown by modern humans and *Pongo*. The bulla-shaped body almost certainly reflects the presence of laryngeal air sacs characteristic of African apes.

One of the significant characteristics of all the great apes (gorilla, chimpanzee and orangutan) is the dramatic alteration in the shape of the skull (and the position of the foramen magnum) as the animal matures. This can be illustrated for the chimpanzee as in Figure 8.15.

Figure 8.17 Chimpanzee Mother and Baby
(Photo: iStock)

Figure 8.18 Additional skeletal material assigned to Selam

So it impossible to be dogmatic as to the species identity of *Australopithecus afarensis* and of *Selam* in particular. If the scapula is from the same creature as the skull then it is possible that *Selam* was a juvenile gorilla[25] or possibly some extinct gorilla-like chimpanzee.

Another characteristic difference between the juvenile and adult ape is posture. The young creature is much more upright and this is reflected in the position of the foramen magnum. This is illustrated in Figures 8.16 and 8.17.

Nobody doubts the juvenile age of *Selam*. She is described as a young female, so it is no wonder that she possesses the skull of a young ape. After the initial discovery, other post-cranial skeletal material was found, including hands and feet and knee joints. Some of this material was very human like (see Figure 8.18). But there can be no certainty that the later material is from the same individual.

8.10 Austalopithecus Sediba

Very recently, Berger *et al.* reported the discovery of two partial skeletons which were given the age of 1.95 to 1.78 million years.[27] The fossils were found in cave deposits at the Malapa site in South Africa. The skeletons were found in close proximity and are thought to be a mother and son that fell to their deaths into the cave. The authors of the report suggest that the remains represent a new species of *Australopithecus* probably descended from *Australopithecus africanus* and demonstrate

features that have more in common with early *Homo* than any other australopithecine species. The team has assigned the name *Australopithecus sediba* to the creatures.

Other palaeoanthropologists, however, are somewhat sceptical of the claims made by the Berger team. For example, in an accompanying article in the same issue of *Science*, it is suggested that the fossils represent an australopithecine which co-existed with the *Homo* genus, since fossils of *Homo* have been conventionally dated as older.[28] Furthermore, in an article in Nature entitled *Claim over 'human ancestor' sparks* *furore,* the authors have been criticised for not taking into account the wealth of variation within *Australopithecus africanus*.[29]

8.11 Paranthropus Boisei

Figure 8.19 An Adult Orangutan (Photo: iStock)

Paranthropus boisei was originally called *Zinjanthropus boisei*. It has been described as an early hominin and the largest of the *Paranthropus* species, and is dated to between 1.2 and 2.6 million years ago in eastern Africa. The fossils were first discovered by anthropologist Mary Leakey in July 1959 at Olduvai Gorge, Tanzania. Mary's son, Richard Leakey considered it to be the first hominin species to use stone tools. Another skull was unearthed in 1969 by Richard at Koobi Fora

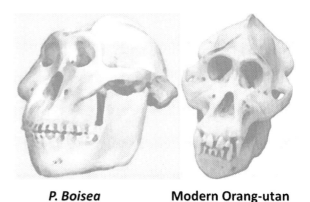

P. Boisea   **Modern Orang-utan**

Figure 8.20 Comparison of Skulls (6)

near the Lake Turkana region. It has been estimated that males weighed 68kg (150lb) and stood 1.3m (4ft 3in) tall, while females weighed 45kg (99lb) and stood 1.05m (3ft 5in) tall. This is exactly the weight and height range

of modern orangutans. The skull morphology of *Paranthropus boisei* is similar to a modern orangutan (see Figure 8.20). As with previous comparisons, the modern animal has more pronounced canine teeth.

Female	2.6-3.5ft (0.8-1.1m)	110 lb (50kg)
Male	3.2-4.5ft (1-1.4m)	200 lb (90kg)

Table 1: Average Height and Weight of the Adult Orangutan

8.12 Homo Habilis

The first specimen assigned to the species *Homo habilis* was designated OH 7 and discovered by the Leakeys in 1960 at Olduvai Gorge, Tanzania, the same region as *Paranthropus boisei*. Louis Leakey was convinced that this was the Olduvai toolmaker he had spent his life looking for, and placed this as a direct human ancestor. In particular, the creature had a relatively large brain, adding weight to the idea that this creature was a nearer relative to *Homo sapiens*.

It has been suggested that:

> It is particularly hard to list the features of *Homo habilis*, because the specimens attributed to habilis (and the reasons the material was placed there) vary widely. The species is a mishmash of traits and specimens, whose composition depends upon what researcher one asks. The simplest way to describe the general features is to describe specimens that are generally considered habilis by most people, and list their relevant traits… *Homo habilis* is a very complicated species to describe. No two researchers attribute all the same specimens as habilis, and few can agree on what traits define habilis, if it is a valid species at all, and even whether or not it belongs in the genus *Homo* or *Australopithecus*. Hopefully, future discoveries and future cladistic analyses of the specimens involved may clear up these issues, or at least better define what belongs in the species.[30]

In 1972, the Leakey team discovered a skull designated KNM-ER 1470 for its registration at the Kenya National Museum in East Rudolf. The skull capacity was initially estimated to be around 800cc, which is relatively large. In addition, the skull had only small eyebrow ridges, no crest, and a significant dome, all typical of the human condition. Furthermore, it had a femur and leg bones very similar to that of modern humans (such as were found a few kilometres away in the same layer).

The biggest problem with this discovery was arriving at a date that "fitted" with evolutionary expectations. The most reasonable estimate based on radiometric analysis dates the strata at 2.61 million years. This is remarkably old for fossils that appear to be so modern. In 1990, Richard Leakey stated:

> If pressed about man's ancestry, I would have to unequivocally say that all we have is a huge question mark. To date, there has been nothing found to truthfully purport as a transitional specie [sic] to man, including Lucy, since 1470 was as old and probably older. If further pressed, I would have to state that there is more evidence to suggest an abrupt arrival of man rather than a gradual process of evolving.[31]

8.13 Homo Erectus

Whereas *Homo habilis* is a fairly ill-defined group that may contain both ancient humans and apes, *Homo erectus* is more straightforward to classify. *Homo erectus* features prominently in the history of paleoanthropology. Dutch anatomist Eugene Dubois first described the species as *Pithecanthropus erectus* (upright ape-man), based on a skullcap and a modern-looking femur found from the bank of the Solo River at Trinil, in central Java.[32] These finds are shown in Figure 8.21. His find is commonly referred to as Java Man and is now classified *Homo erectus*.

In July 1984, a relatively complete skeleton of a very human-like 12-year-old boy was discovered at Lake Turkana in Kenya and classified as *Homo erectus*. The height of the boy is estimated at 160cm (5ft 3in) tall with a brain capacity of 880cc. Accepting that the individual had not reached maturity, it has been estimated that in adulthood, the boy would have grown to be 185cm (6ft 1in) tall with a brain capacity of 910cc. The skeleton of this child is like that of a modern human in all respects except for certain details of the skull, namely, a low forehead and pronounced brow ridges. Richard Leakey said: "This boy would go unnoticed in a crowd today."

New discoveries in 2007 suggest that *Homo habilis* and *Homo erectus* coexisted and may be separate lineages from a common ancestor.[33] This research team found the complete skull of *Homo erectus* within walking distance of an upper jaw of *Homo habilis* that had been found previously in 2000 in the same strata. Fred Spoor, professor of evolutionary anatomy at University College, London, and one of the co-authors, commented:

> The two species lived near each other, but probably didn't interact, each having its own "ecological niche," *Homo habilis* was likely more vegetarian while *Homo erectus* ate some meat... they'd just avoid each other, they don't feel comfortable in each other's company. There remains some still-undiscovered common ancestor that probably lived 2 million to 3 million years ago, a time that has not left much fossil record. Overall what it paints for human evolution is a chaotic kind of looking evolutionary tree rather than this heroic march that you see with the cartoons of an early ancestor evolving into some intermediate and eventually unto us.[33]

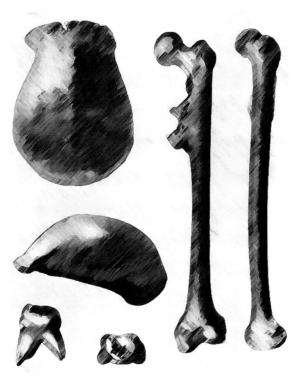

Figure 8.21 The remains of Java Man

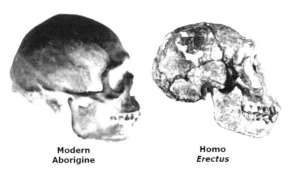

Modern Aborigine   Homo Erectus

Figure 8.22 Comparison of Skulls (7)

Furthermore, skulls of both modern and ancient native Australian aborigines have been shown to possess characteristics very similar to *Homo erectus*.[34,35] Remains dated between 10,000 and 30,000 years ago and even very recently have been found to differ in only one of the seven anatomical points of the skull (in terms of cranial-vault thickness) from their counterparts in *Homo erectus*. This is illustrated in Figure 8.22.

According to Vanhollebeke:

> The controversial Pintubi-1 skull of Australia is a paradox of paleoanthropology. As a hominid fossil, it's so young that it has been assigned to a tribe that survived into the last century - a modern aboriginal skull. Yet its morphology could be described as archaic. The skull's history is shrouded in mystery (not unlike others from the down under). Even without documentation, its age and Australoid identity are indisputable. The man it inhabited lived very recently (in paleo-terms), likely in the 1800s or later. It is in perfect condition and shows no signs of antiquity. The skull was discovered or obtained around 1905 near the lower Darling River in New South Wales, Australia. Beyond that, all we are able to determine is that it is said to be a large adult 50 year old male from the Pintubi tribe.[36]

There would seem to be little doubt that the fossils assigned to *Homo erectus* are truly human and are still represented today in so-called primitive tribes such as the pure Aborigines of Australia. In this situation, the connection with the more ancient finds in Java and China are totally consistent geographically.

8.14 Neanderthal Man

Figure 8.23 Skeleton of a Neanderthal man found in La Grotte de Clamouse in France (Photo: iStock)

Figure 8.24 Popular representation of the Neanderthal Man[37]

In 1856, three years before the publication of *The Origin of Species*, a schoolteacher, Johann Fuhlrott discovered a partial skeleton in the Neander Valley near to Düsseldorf in Germany, The skeleton comprised a skullcap, thighbones, part of a pelvis, some ribs, and some arm and shoulder bones and lay in a small cave at Feldhofer. An initial examination by Professor Schaafhausen concluded that the skeleton was a normal human. Since that time, there have been many more similar discoveries. One such discovery was found in La Grotte de Clamouse in France and is shown in Figure 8.23.

However, in 1908, Professor Boule of the Institute of Human Paleontology in Paris declared Neanderthal an ape-man because of his low eyebrow ridges and the stooped posture of some of the specimens. This view was to predominate throughout the 20th Century and led to imaginative artistic representations of the cave man such as shown in Figure 8.24.

The Neanderthal group is now regarded as an extinct species of the *Homo* genus and is either classified as a subspecies of humans (*Homo sapiens neanderthalensis*) or as a separate species (*Homo neanderthalensis*). Neanderthal stone tools provide evidence of their wide distribution in places where skeletal remains have not been found.

Neanderthal cranial capacity was much larger than that of modern humans. On average, the height of Neanderthals was comparable to contemporaneous *Homo sapiens.* Neanderthal males stood about 165–168cm tall (about 5ft 5in) and were heavily built with robust bone structure. They were much stronger than their human contemporaries, having particularly strong arms and hands. Females stood about 152–156cm tall (about 5ft 1in).

8.15 Further Questions

1   Why is nearly every chimp-like or gorilla-like fossil assigned to a human lineage?

2   How would theories of human origins have to change if artefacts such as the Laetoli footprints were recognised as human?

3   Is there any kind of specimen that could prove whether humans and chimps have a common ancestor or not?

Chapter 8 Endnotes

1   Brunet M *et al.* (2002) *A new hominid from the Upper Miocene of Chad, Central Africa* Nature 418:145–51

2   http://www.paleoanthro.org/journal/content/PA20060036.pdf

3   http://www.uwyo.edu/bioanth/Docs/Ahern05-FMposition.pdf

4   Senut, B *et al.* (2001) *First hominid from the Miocene (Lukeino Formation, Kenya)* Comptes Rendus de l'Académie de Sciences 332:137–44

5   http://igs.indiana.edu/geology/fossils/usingfossils/index.cfm

6   http://news.bbc.co.uk/2/hi/science/nature/4187991.stm

7   Haile-Selassie Y *et al.* (2004) *Late Miocene Teeth from Middle Awash, Ethiopia, and Early Hominid Dental Evolution* Science 303: 1503–5

8   There is a great deal of confusion as to whether this knee joint was ever assigned to the subsequent find of Lucy's partial skeleton by Johanson himself. Lucy's skeletal remains do not possess any knee joint (or hands and feet). Common sense dictates that the knee joint is from a separate individual and is almost certainly human.

9   Wolpoff, MH (1983) *Lucy's little legs* Journal of Human Evolution 12:443-53

10   There is a great deal of controversy over the exact characteristics of the partial hip recovered by Johanson and his team. The original fossil was greatly distorted by the process of fossilisation and had to be reconstructed by Owen Lovejoy, Professor of Anthropology at Kent State University.

11   Stern J, Sussman R (1983) American Journal of Physical Anthropology 60:279-17

12   Lovejoy CO The Natural History of Human Gait and Posture, Part 1. Spine and Pelvis Gait and Posture (2005) 21:95-112

13   After Lewin R (1999) Human Evolution: An Illustrated Introduction (Paperback) 4th edition Blackwell Science; page 95. It needs to be appreciated that the representation of the hip and leg of Lucy is a compilation of material from various sources. The hip is based on the reconstruction of the partial hip bones discovered by Johanson in 1974. The knee is based on the separate and earlier find of Johanson in 1973. The feet are representative of creatures (almost certainly human) who could produce footprints like those discovered at Laetoli.

14   http://www.web-articles.info/e/a/title/Lower-limb-in-human-body/

15   http://www.trueorigin.org/knee.asp

16   *Analysis of the human and ape foot during bipedal standing with implications for the evolution of the foot* Journal of Biomechanics 37:1831-6

17   Tuttle R (1991) *Did a. afarensis make the Laetoli G footprint trails?* Amer. Journal of Phys. Anthropology supplement: 175

18   Tuttle R (1990) Natural History, page 60

19   Raichlen DA *et al. Laetoli Footprints Preserve Earliest Direct Evidence of Human-Like Bipedal Biomechanics.* PLoS ONE (2010) 5: e9769

20   Dart RA (1925) *Australopithecus africanus: the man-ape of South Africa.* Nature: 115:195-9

21   Alemseged Z *et al.* (2006) *A juvenile early hominin skeleton from Dikika, Ethiopia* Nature 443, 296-301

22   http://flickr.com/photos/51035610238@N01/248390730/

23   http://en.wikipedia.org/wiki/Raymond_Dart

24   http://en.wikipedia.org/wiki/Hyoid_bone

25   http://flickr.com/photos/jamiedecesare/2079874305/

26   Adapted from Gould SJ (1977) Ontogeny and Phylogeny Belknap (Harvard University Press) page 355

27   Berger, LR *et al.* Australopithecus sediba: A New Species of Homo-Like Australopith from South Africa Science (2010) 328:195–204

28   Candidate Human Ancestor From South Africa Sparks Praise and Debate Science (2010) 328:154–5

29   Claim over 'human ancestor' sparks furore Nature News (2010) 10:1038

30   http://www.archaeologyinfo.com/homohabilis.htm

31   http://www.detectingdesign.com/earlyman.html

32   Shipman P (2002) *The Man Who Found the Missing Link.* New York, Simon and Schuster

33   F. Spoor, M. G. Leakey, P. N. Gathogo, F. H. Brown, S. C. Antón, I. McDougall, C. Kiarie, F. K. Manthi & L. N. Leakey (2007) *Implications of new early Homo fossils from Ileret, east of Lake Turkana, Kenya* Nature 448 (448):688–91

34   http://www.canovan.com/HumanOrigin/PINTUBI-1/PINTUBI-1.htm

35   http://www.canovan.com/HumanOrigin/kow/kowswamp.htm

36   http://www.canovan.com/HumanOrigin/PINTUBI-1/PINTUBI-1.htm

37   Depiction of a Neanderthal man from a 1909 French publication

Summary

We have now reached the end of our survey of the origins of the living world. We have traced the path of the conventional scientific account of how the whole diversity of living organisms might have developed from almost nothing – that is, from non-living chemicals and physical energy through to coordinated molecular systems, bacteria, worms, fish, dinosaurs, birds, mammals and human beings. We have traced this path and seen how it is presented as a series of stepping stones. Although some stones appear to be a long way from previous ones, research and speculation continue in attempts to narrow the distance between them, even to present them as a continuous, inexorable path. However this is not the way the authors of this book see the observed evidence. We believe that a better picture is presented by that of a chain of islands. Each island certainly has its promontories and its beaches, and the tides rise and fall, but there can be no doubt that these are distinct islands separated by sea.

Along our journey there have been many questions to ponder. Most of the problems that

Evidence of origins can appear like separate islands
(Photo: ©)

this book has outlined for the conventional story of evolution are not minor challenges to find missing links in an otherwise plausible account. Rather, they point out the huge qualitative differences between different realms of biological diversity and complexity. We may know how big a ribosome is compared to a ribose molecule, but to step across this

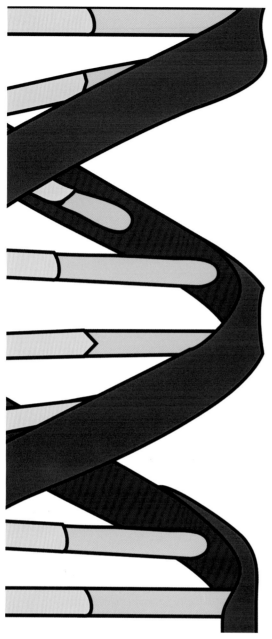
DNA Double Helix (Photo: ©)

simple size difference is to step between two worlds – from chemistry to biology. Our story began in Chapter 2, as we explored the impasse of chemical evolution. When we move from the random mixtures of chemicals in origin-of-life experiments to a highly-ordered, tightly controlled string of bases in an mRNA molecule on its way out of a nucleus, we are not just looking at simple vs. complex chemistry; this is the fundamental difference between living and non-living systems.

We had little to say about the origins of living cells, since even the conventional account is a sea of speculation. The gulf between RNA molecules that might build up on clays or zinc deposits and the functioning of the simplest conceivable living cell is enormous, and the conventional story currently seems to resort to miracles or extraterrestrial gifts. This is a good point to ask ourselves whether we really have faith that the origin of life problem will eventually be salvaged to physical and chemical respectability – and whether researchers can really discover what actually happened by speculative laboratory experiments.

In Chapter 3 we saw how DNA replication is not just chemistry. Indeed, the more research advances in molecular biology, the more intricate is our picture of complex structures and functions within the cell. Similarly, research on the structure of organisms' genomes is revealing unimagined systems of complex regulation. The Darwinian paradigm has produced singularly unimaginative interpretations of the genome, with emphasis on junk DNA, ubiquitous pseudogenes and viral fossils, whereas a design paradigm suggests exciting programmes of research relating to topics such as control theory and phenotypic plasticity. There is also a philosophical problem with the Darwinian paradigm for genetics. DNA molecules must be seen as carriers of information if we are to understand their function in coding for proteins and affecting the phenotypes of organisms. This perspective calls for an explanation of the origin of new information, and the laws of mutation and natural selection do not seem to do this job, however good they may be for managing the physical structure of existing genetic material.

In Chapter 4 we learnt how stromatolites are found in rock formations apparently dating from our planet's earliest days. This only makes the origins of living cells more mysterious – not to mention the fact that stromatolites presumably lived by the biochemical marvel that is photosynthesis. More generally, the fossil record is most remarkable for what it does not document. It frequently presents us

Trilobite Fossils[1] (Photo: ©)

with whole assemblages of complex organisms without offering candidates for evolutionary antecedents.

The so-called Cambrian Explosion surprises us by the diversity of the body-plans of animals that are revealed in these ancient rock layers. It also raises the puzzle of how the functional complexity at the base of such a radiation could have built up so quickly – exoskeletons, diverse means of locomotion, nervous systems, and compound eyes. The origin of fish and other chordates (as discussed in Chapter 5) only becomes more mysterious with recent discoveries of Cambrian fish and with little consensus among molecular phylogenetic trees about how chordates could be related to other deuterostome phyla.

In the rest of the story, Chapters 5, 6 and 7 required us to imagine how aquatic animals could have begun to live on land, how land animals could begin taking to the air in flight, and how mammals could have emerged from reptiles. Each of these major "island-hopping" transitions is the subject of much speculation among evolutionary biologists.

The evolutionary stories that are offered tend to describe progress along sequences of fossils that have been arranged according to morphological similarities – like writing a story to fit someone else's holiday snaps. By contrast, the kind of hypotheses really needed are ones that also suggest how the diverse anatomical and physiological adaptations of tetrapods, birds and mammals could come about in gradual, uncoordinated steps so that every single one of the animals in which they occurred would be well adapted to its environment and able to compete successfully with other individuals and other species.

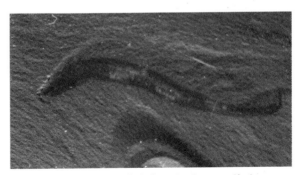

Fossil specimen of Pikaia fom the Burgess Shale on display at the Smithsonian in Washington, DC (Photo: ©)

Charles Darwin as an old man (Photo: ©)

Aquatic and Terrestrial Mammals[5] (Photo: ©)

By now we may find it easier to believe impossible things, but once we look at such adaptations as the digits of tetrapod limbs and their breathing apparatus, the jointed rib-cage and supracoracoideus pulley system of birds, or the integrated regulatory systems of mammals, the story-telling looks very ambitious indeed. To believe the stories already being told based on fossils requires considerable faith. In particular, to believe that parallel stories can be told to account for the stepwise evolution of anatomical and physiological systems as Darwinian innovations is surely beyond credibility for anyone who retains an open mind. We need to remember that according to the Darwinian hypothesis, such innovations are unprecedented, undirected and uncalled for.

Finally, the evolution of humans from apes is surprisingly fraught with obstacles. Chapter 8 mentioned the major problems of hominoid evolution from a skeletal point of view, as well as some of the puzzles of dating and biogeography. However, this seemingly trivial step calls for reflection on what it is to be human, and on the significance of our science. Are humans basically one species that has evolved out of laws of physics and chemistry among many other species? Are our minds essentially variations on the minds of hominoids? If the Western population is really educated to believe that humans are basically animals that have created knowledge and culture out of nothing, then people may ask why the brains of Homo sapiens are any more reliable than the brains of *Pan* or of *Ornithorhyncus*. Then we may find that our precious biological insights begin to be placed alongside the insights of other species – and if we doubt that chimpanzees, platypus or the amphioxus have true knowledge, we must ask what kind of knowledge humans really have. While no one disputes that humans are biologically one species among many, does a purely evolutionary origin allow for human knowledge to be true and for human art, love and ethics to be real?

So the greatest casualty in the story of origins by Darwinian evolution is the richness of biological diversity, and ultimately the significance of human culture – including science. The main theme in the story that we have grappled with is reductionism. Reductionism is the art of ignoring the distinctive features of one kind of structure in order to claim that it is nothing but a complex version of something that is in reality completely different. It is a favourite

An artistic representation of ancient man[2] (Photo: ©)

tool in many academic pursuits, yet it ends up impoverishing the distinct academic fields of study – first other people's disciplines and then our own. So the reductionism of Enlightenment philosophers has long demoted the "arts" as less important than the "sciences", and the "softer" sciences (biology, psychology, sociology) as inferior to the "hard" sciences (chemistry and physics). More recently, the evolutionary reductionist Richard Dawkins pondered why zoology is still a minority subject at universities[3] and people such as Daniel Dennett and Steven Pinker have attempted to reduce human understanding to evolutionary psychology.[4] But reductionism becomes self refuting once we have reduced ourselves and our thoughts and feelings to something other than what we take them to be in practice. If someone believes that life arose from chemistry by the laws of physics and natural selection and sees their brain as just a complicated end-product of this, can they continue to believe that their thoughts are true apart from helping them survive? Indeed, can

their consciousness be anything other than a "feeling" of the laws of physics?

Most people will acknowledge that today's evolutionary story of gradual progress seems to run against heavy odds and contains ambitious speculation. Its attraction is so great to those who are committed to a naturalistic worldview that the probabilities and gaps probably do not matter. However, the authors of this book have argued that the Darwinian story is not only incredible, it is also an inadequate framework for biological research, for scientific understanding and for teaching new generations of scientists, humanitarians, artists – in short, this paradigm is a worldview that sells students short as real human beings. Only time will reveal the effects on our culture more broadly, but the students of today do not need to be subjects in this psychological experiment themselves. They can join the growing ranks of those who look for a richer, more human and more fulfilling approach to science.

Summary Endnotes

1   The trilobites in the top row are likely from Morocco and of order Phacopida. The bottom left hand trilobite is Elrathia kingi (order Ptychopariida), a common Cambrian trilobite from Utah (USA). This one's probably just a moult as the "free cheeks" are missing. The other two small ones are Peronopsis species (order Agnostida), also from Utah.

2   Restoration by Amedee Forestier of the Rhodesian man whose skull was discovered in 1921.

3   Dawkins, R (1976) The Selfish Gene, Oxford University Press

4   Dennet, D (2006) Breaking the Spell, Viking (Penguin); Pinker, S. (1997) How the Mind Works, Norton & Co.

Index

About the Authors

Geoff Barnard

Andy McIntosh

Stephen Taylor

Dr Geoff Barnard

PhD, MA

Geoff Barnard, author of over 100 academic papers and articles, has a PhD in Biochemistry from the University of London and an MA in Theology from University of Southampton. He has been a professional biochemist for over 40 years, a Senior Lecturer in Biological Sciences at three UK Universities and a regular visiting scientist at the Weizmann Institute of Science in Israel. His last academic position in the UK was as a Senior Research Scientist in the Department of Veterinary Medicine, University of Cambridge, a position he held for over seven years. He now lives in Israel and is employed as a Senior Scientist in the Diagnostics Industry.

Professor Andy McIntosh

DSc, FIMA, C.Math, FEI, C.Eng, FInstP, MIGEM, FRAeS

Andy McIntosh holds an emeritus chair in Thermodynamics and Combustion Theory, (University of Leeds) and has lectured and researched in these fields for over 20 years. Author of over 180 papers and articles, he has a PhD from the aerodynamics department of what was then Cranfield Institute of Technology (now Cranfield University), a DSc in Applied Mathematics (University of Wales) and in the last few years has been involved in research in the area of biomimetics where the minute combustion chamber of the bombardier beetle has inspired a patented novel spray technology. This research was awarded the 2010 Times Higher Educational award for the Outstanding Contribution to Innovation and Technology.

Dr Steve Taylor

B.Sc, ACGI, MEng, PhD, CEng, FIEE, FInstP

Steve Taylor is a Reader at the University of Liverpool and head of the mass spectrometry research group in the School of Electrical Engineering, Electronics and Computer Science. Teaching duties include final year honours courses in Electromagnetism and MEMS Design. Other research interests include nanotechnology of the physical layer and quantum information processing using ion traps. He is a reviewer for several academic journals and is author or co-author of over 230 articles, patents or publications in the open scientific literature. He holds a Fellowship of the Electrical Research Association (ERA). He acts as consultant to several UK companies and is founder and director of a University spin-out company.

The authors wish to thank all those who have contributed to and supported the production of this work in any way.

Each of the authors writes in a private capacity and the views expressed are not necessarily those of the institutions where they are employed.

Commendations

Edgar Andrews

BSc, PhD, DSc, FInstP, FIMMM, CEng, Chas.
Emeritus Professor of Materials
University of London

This book reaches the parts that other treatments of origins and evolution ignore, exposing the contentious nature of much that is superficially received and taught as 'fact' in these areas of study. Here is a seriously in-depth treatment of the scientific problems and perplexities facing naturalistic accounts of causation - whether in origin-of-life studies, molecular genetics, evolutionary biology, fossils or anthropology (human origins). This well-presented mine of information won't be found in standard texts yet needs to be known by all who teach and study science and biology.

Sylvia Baker

BSc (Hons) (Biology) MSc (Radiation Biology) PhD (Education)

I can heartily recommend this book. It provides a much needed balance to the one-sided view of the evidence for evolution which is the current fare for the nation's school children and TV viewers. The well-expressed material it contains will help the reader to evaluate the evidence and will thereby also train him or her to think as a scientist should.

Stuart Burgess

BSc, PhD(Brun), CEng, FIMechE
Professor of Engineering Design
University of Bristol

Examining the Evidence focuses on the areas that are the biggest challenge to evolution such as the origin of life, the origin of birds and the origin of man. The authors are very well qualified in biology, physics and chemistry and they use their expert knowledge to explain clearly why evolutionary theory cannot explain the complexity and diversity of life. Anyone who is interested to know where the evidence for origins leads must read this book.

Nick Cowan

MA (Cantab), P.G.Cert.Ed
Retired Chemistry Master

The history of science shows us that real advances are often only made when existing status quo paradigms are questioned and challenged. Darwinian evolution is a theory that needs to come under such scrutiny, lest it become a sacred cow that no-one dares to disbelieve. This book is a courageous attempt to examine the evolutionary worldview in the light of recent advances in Biochemistry and other scientific disciplines. Anyone on the side of truth, from the A-level Biology student upwards, will be impressed by its desire to liberate science from an evolutionary straitjacket.

Norman C. Nevin

OBE BSc, MD, FRCPath, FPHM, FRCPE FRCP
Emeritus Professor of Medical Genetics
Queen's University, Belfast

Examining the Evidence considers the question of origins; the origin of life, the origin of genetic information within the cell, and the origins of fish, birds, mammals and man.

The most persuasive evidence is that for the origin of information within the cell. It is now clear that the human genome is not just a string of letters spelling out a linear series of instruction. The genome functions as a multilayered hierarchical integrated system. The DNA code is only one layer of information. Since the completion of the Human Gene Project in 2003, numerous scientific publications have provided evidence of other layers of cellular information – non-protein coding DNA (previously referred to as 'junk DNA'), slicing code, chromatin, folding patterns of proteins and the position of the chromosome within the cell. It is argued that as information cannot be derived from the material medium or indeed, from the code itself, the origin of information suggests an intelligent source for both the code and the message.

The authors simply make an appeal for the reader to examine the evidence and to follow where it leads. They conclude that the Darwinian explanation for origins is not yet substantiated. I believe this easy-to-read little volume is a must-read for every biology teacher and student.

Dr Alastair Noble

BSc PhD
Former Inspector of Schools, Scotland, and Head of Educational Services, South Ayrshire

This remarkable book considers in detail the major areas of scientific evidence for the evolutionary theory of life's origin and development. Its conclusion is often disturbing: evolutionary speculation often passes for certain scientific fact. If as student or teacher you wish to go, in the spirit of scientific enquiry, where the evidence leads, this book will help you greatly in your study.

Colin Reeves

MPhil PhD CStat
Emeritus Professor of Operational Research
Coventry University

Darwinian evolution is the ruling scientific paradigm of our time, yet any attempt to raise questions about the scientific evidence on which it is supposed to be based creates a furore. This book asks questions about this evidence – questions that the standard textbooks ignore or dismiss too easily.

Barnard, McIntosh and Taylor explain carefully the conventional accounts of some of the major steps in the Darwinian chain. Starting with the origin of life itself, they discuss the crucial issue of information and complexity before proceeding to examine the purported dinosaur/bird transition and the origins of mammals and humans. At the end of each chapter they suggest further questions for study, and supplement the general approach with detailed case studies.

This is no simplistic anti-evolutionary tract and religious objections to Darwinism are eschewed – the focus is clearly on the science. The authors carefully document their sources and display their own expertise in the way they explain the scientific implications. There is no dumbing-down concession for the sake of a good story, and it is fair to say that some degree of scientific knowledge is assumed of the reader.

So who should study this book? Clearly, the reader needs to be scientifically literate, but also, and most importantly, should be open-minded. The questions raised are serious, and deserve to be considered in like manner, without appeals to authority. The standard hand-waving "explanations" of evolutionary theory have to be examined at the level of scientific detail and that is what this book does so impressively. It is highly recommended for A-level science students and their teachers, undergraduates, and anyone willing to acquire the scientific understanding needed to engage with these highly important questions.

The title is apt: the book certainly "does what it says on the tin", but beyond that, it will help to equip readers themselves with the ability to ask questions in a proper scientific manner. It is therefore also a valuable contribution to the training of the next generation of scientists.

David J. Tyler

PhD, MSc, BSc
Reader
Manchester Metropolitan University

In accessible language, the authors succeed admirably in showing that the conventional account of evolution fails when confronted with empirical evidence. The implications are serious for science, as the history of Darwinism is littered with unfruitful research. This book demonstrates clearly that the case against molecules-to-man evolution is based on a solid scientific foundation, and this same evidence points to a new paradigm in which information and design is central.

John C. Walton

BSc, PhD, DSc CChem, FRSC, FRSE
Research Professor of Chemistry
University of St. Andrews

This crisply written book provides a fresh new approach to crucial aspects of the origins debate. The detailed and well-illustrated accounts of key topics such as fossil sequences, gene expression and chemical evolution bring fascinating new factors to light. The narrative highlights the contradictions and conundrums faced by conventional evolutionary scenarios which are stalled in a sea of speculation. Reductionist explanations of the origin of the information content of genomes face extreme difficulties; design emerges as a better alternative. *Examining the Evidence* shows that the 'closed ranks' stance of the evolutionary establishment is unsustainable.

Continues

Tim Wells

BSc, PhD
Senior Lecturer in Neuroendocrinology
School of Biosciences, Cardiff University

A scientific theory is only as good as its supporting evidence and the best scientists continue to challenge accepted paradigms until a unifying theory, however unpopular, explains all the data. In this thought-provoking review the authors reveal that, when it come to verifiable evidence, Neo-Darwinian dogma is at best a very shaky stack of cards, and at worst a sophistry.